The Baby Sleep Bible

Jo Wiltshire

The
Baby Sleep
Bible

Choosing what's right for you and your baby

white
LADDER

This edition first published in Great Britain 2009 by
Crimson Publishing, a division of Crimson Business Ltd
Westminster House
Kew Road
Richmond
Surrey
TW9 2ND

A catalogue record for this book is available from the British
Library.

ISBN 978 1 90541 059 0

Printed and bound by LegoPrint SpA, Trento

Acknowledgements

My first thanks go to my amazing children Evie and Charlie. Both have developed a wonderful ability to relish the joy of sleep. I can't take much credit for it – at least, not for anything I have actually done on purpose. A friend of mine did give me the nickname 'the sloth' a long time ago, though, so maybe I have endowed them both with some kind of golden sleep gene. I like to think it is that, rather than an intense desire on my part to get downstairs in time for *EastEnders* which has led to an ingrained 7pm 'switch off' in their psyches.

I also thank my husband Lewis. He lifts our spirits, makes the children laugh like drains, cooks wonderful meals, and does a mean Mick Jagger impression. More pertinently, he is a truly wonderful, joyous and hands-on father, and gets up with unfailing good humour whenever I pretend not to hear Charlie calling early on Saturday mornings...

My mother, Annie, and Colin have been absolute rocks – they look after us, give us their all, and make everything work. They have also given me the time to write this book. Thank you.

Thank you too to Lew's mother Chris, who steps in with unshakeable good humour and an ever-open door when needed, to my lovely father Tony and my sister Lindsey, and to the rest of our families who we love very much. Also thank you to anyone who has taken pity on my husband and children on days when I have been writing this book, and fed and watered them for me (especially Max, Dave and Estelle!). And to Lily the whippet for keeping me company on long writing days.

Thank you to Roni Jay. I wish her and her boys lots of happy times in the future. And thank you to Beth and everyone at White Ladder.

And, very importantly, thank you to the parents who inspired and contributed to this book; the parents who have tried it all, who have yearned for sleep, who have experimented sleeping every which way until they found something that worked. And who were prepared to share it all – even the bad bits. Thank you to:

Dalvinder, Conrad, Amber, India and Jasmine; Nikki, Gary and George; Jo, Phil, Archie and Charlotte; Sandra, Graham, Ben and Toby; Jane, Ant and Lola; Maxine, Dave, Marnie and Freddy; Carrie, Paul and Jake; Mary-anne, Nigel, Kitty and Finn; Becky, James and Lois; Jessica, Will and Tessa; Dan, Jo and Talise; Callie, Andrew, Lily, James and Sophia; Lisa, James, Fionn and Bridget; Caroline, Graham, Heather and Murray; Kim and Sasha; Laura, Andy, Max and James; Gill, Alex, Stanley and Poppy; Tania, Tom, Rebecca, Ashley and Vincent; Gemma, Richard, Sara and Phoebe; Jenny, Matt, Luke and Perry; Kerry, Jon and Mason; and Maria, Hasan, Zehra, Ceyda and Nadia.

Lastly, thank you to anyone who reads this. I hope it helps, even a little bit. And I hope they sleep, even a little bit. And hopefully a lot. Good luck!

Contents

Foreword

> 66 Sleep is like the unicorn — it is rumoured to exist, but I doubt I will see any.
>
> Anonymous 99

When I first brought home my perfect baby daughter from the hospital, I entered my living room, which was filled with balloons and a Welcome Home banner (sweet husband), and was hit by that first-time-parent wobbly feeling: Well, here we are. She's so gorgeous! I'm so tired. What if she won't sleep? And in the following days, when I was plunged into that first madness of breastfeeding, family visits, nappies and sore everything, that one thing remained: please – tell me, please – where have they put the Off button? Surely, surely she has one tucked away somewhere, on her back near the battery opening, maybe, just like a baby doll?

I never found that Off button. What I found instead was a whole range of books which, with their reassuringly glossy covers and authoritative tones, calmed me with their promises that sleep was, despite all evidence to the contrary, a realistic prospect.

The only problem was that nobody seemed to agree on exactly how this was to be achieved. Each expert was equally adamant in their stance – so which way should one go?

Family bed, all cosy in a fug of natural bonding? Baby slings and constant cuddles and back to nature? Or calm, peaceful nurseries, with blackout blinds and no eye contact and the quiet tick of a reassuring routine? Or Moses baskets, or controlled crying, or timetables, or baby massage, or cot 'sidecar' arrangements, or back-patting precisely every 15 minutes, or... help!

It seemed to me that you had to take a deep breath, pick an expert and then stick to their advice – rigidly. There was no room for digression, for peering over the parapet. This was Baby Sleep War – and you had to know which side you were on.

Now, some years later and with an equally perfect (in my completely unbiased eyes) baby son to add to the sleep mix, I feel somewhat differently. Actually, I was one of those parents who never did make that leap firmly off the fence - I ended up taking bits of advice from both sides and making them work for me. Along the way, I gathered a ton of information about what works on the sleep front. And it's apparent, not just from my own experience but from that of other parents - real parents who have paced real landings tearing out real hair and crying with desperation into real pillows - that what is needed is a tailored approach.

Different children sleep in different ways. Different families need, want and are forced into different routines. Sleep isn't – and cannot be – a blanket issue (excuse the pun).

So this book isn't going to shout at you, nor is it going to spy on you if you sneak into your baby's nursery a minute before you are supposed to go in and give her a cuddle. With or without eye contact. And it's not going to frown if you decide you need a night without that demanding little body occupying the space between you and your husband. In other words, it's not going to tell you what to do. It's simply going to tell you what you *can* do. What the options are. Which ones might be right for you - and, if they appeal to you, how the experts tell you to make them work, and how other parents found them.

If you need a Baby Sleep approach that is just right for *your* family and *your* baby, read *The Baby Sleep Bible*. And then hopefully you will have lots of peaceful evenings for other bedtime reading... or even some sleep of your own.

You can contact Jo at her website: www.jowiltshire.com

Introduction

WHICH BABY SLEEP APPROACH WILL SUIT YOU?

❝ The best bridge between despair and hope is a good night's sleep.

E Joseph Cossman

❞

If you give birth away from home, for example in a hospital or midwifery unit, soon enough you will be ejected into the world with your obligatory baby car seat and your tiny bundle of joy. The crazy optimistic excitement of this situation usually extends from the point the mother has managed to gingerly slide herself into the back seat of the car without overly traumatising any of her sore bits to the point you have closed your front door, put the car seat down on the living room floor and suddenly realised – hang on, we've come away without the instructions!

At first, it comes as something of a shock that the healthcare professionals allowed you to leave the premises with your baby without taking an exam, or undergoing an intensive crash course in baby care.

But, being bereft of those instructions, you take a deep breath and get on with it. And somewhere during the next few hours, days and months, you discover that in fact, taking home a new baby is something akin to taking home a fantastic state-of-the-art plasma television from the electrical store, opening the box, and finding not just one set of instructions, but seven or eight.

'Take your pick!' you are advised as you unfold the booklets. 'Here are all the leads, the connectors, the cables. Now, just choose any method of putting them all together. Whichever you pick, you should eventually get a picture – but be prepared for lots of tears along the way. Oh, and by the way, your neighbour will probably pop round mid-assembly and tell you smugly that you should have picked a different set of instructions, because the ones you chose are bound to send your TV up in smoke when it grows up...'

We have all heard of some of the better-known methods of getting a baby to sleep. Gina Ford, Richard Ferber, William Sears, the Baby Whisperer – such names have become so mythical to parents that they sum up whole swathes of sleep suggestions, even those that didn't even originate with the 'guru' concerned. These experts have even become nouns and verbs – 'We've been doing a Gina', you might hear, or 'Have they tried Ferberising her?'

Most Baby Sleep experts build an approach based on an underlying belief that babies thrive on routine, for example, or that babies who are allowed to sleep in a family bed are easier to get to sleep and will grow up to be more secure adults.

Many approaches fall into either the 'no tears' category – not letting a baby cry to sleep – or the 'cry-it-out' category – using varying degrees of 'controlled' crying to achieve independent sleep.

The problem is that most of these methods differ widely in their approach, and therefore in their ethos. In addition the underlying beliefs are packed with emotive judgements, sometimes intentional, sometimes maybe not, which make choosing between them a minefield of guilt and worry for parents. Who doesn't want their precious baby to feel secure? To be emotionally stable and to feel loved? To be confident and independent? But how can a parent guarantee all these things when they have to choose between methods?

Do you have to stick to one method exclusively? Or can you cherry pick the best bits of different methods?

After years of debate over which method is best, experts finally came out with a new message that declared that just about all the techniques work, as long as you pick one and stick with it.

Most of the approaches reviewed in the October 2006 issue of the journal *Sleep* were supported by evidence that they resulted in infants and toddlers learning to fall asleep independently at bedtime and when they woke during the night. But the key was 'parents being consistent', according to senior review author Dr Jodi A Mindell, a psychology professor at Saint Joseph's University in Philadelphia, USA, and chair of the task force organised by the American Academy of Sleep Medicine to assess the techniques (*The New York Times*, 12 December 2006). 'They need to pick a plan they can absolutely follow through on,' she said.

So – a consistent approach is best. But even the experts admit that there is room for diversity here regarding exactly which method you should go with. Dr Richard Ferber, of the 'Ferberising' fame strongly linked with the cry-it-out method, has agreed on record that no single approach works for all children, and that the approach should be tailored to the family and child. 'When an intervention is chosen that works not only for the child's problems but for the family's philosophy of child-rearing, it's going to work that much better,' he said.

And my belief too is that there is *no one right way*. What there is, instead, is a right way for *you, your family*, and *your baby*.

Your lifestyle, work commitments, level of external support and general approach to life will determine to some extent the way that is right for you. The rest will come from your baby – ask any parent if they think their newborn is a blank canvas or actually comes to us as a ready-formed little person with her own pre-determined personality and likes and dislikes, and they will tell you it's the latter. You get what you get – now work around it! It may even mean that what worked for your first child just rubs your second child the wrong way – you may need to change approaches. But there will be *one* way that works, even if you have to give several a go.

And once you have found a method that suits your child, try to give it a chance. Switching between methods will probably just leave your child unsettled and you exhausted. Persistence and the comfort of the familiar can work wonders!

HOW TO USE THIS BOOK

Sleep is an issue that from day one can make parents feel inadequate, desperate and often rather judged. It is an issue that all parents have to tackle – even the parents of the most angelic sleepers are still under pressure to choose an approach, and to find a way to allow their baby's sleep pattern to fit in with family life.

This book aims to lay out the options for you, tell you what kinds of babies and families the various approaches might suit, give you some top real-life tips from real parents who have tried the approaches – and then let you choose what you would like to follow.

The book is intended to be a friendly, useful voice of reason for those times you feel you can't even lift an eyelid any more. Each chapter tackles one of the big sleep issues – the early days and settling in, sleeping through the night, moving into a nursery, and naps, holiday sleeping and general night-time disruption. Within each chapter, these issues are discussed from the viewpoint of four different approaches:

- Back to Nature
- By the Clock
- Flexi-Sleeping
- Multiple Madness

The four approaches are briefly discussed below.

Back to Nature

Attachment parenting, co-sleeping and the Family Bed

The Back to Nature approach is suitable for families who like lots of close bodily contact and physical bonding. It centres on keeping your baby close to you, in a sling during the day, and encourages families to sleep together in a big bed or in a bed with a 'sidecar'-style cot next to it. It appeals to parents who like natural babycare methods, who feel at ease with a demonstrative lifestyle, and who don't demand much 'me time'. It might not suit people who need a certain chunk of the day away from their baby, either to work or to relax.

" I thought I might use the Gina Ford sleep control method, which seemed to be in vogue, but in the end instinct took over. I just wanted to nurture her, love her, cherish her, protect her, never be apart from her! It was so special, and I entered into a world where we both made our own timetables according to how we both felt.

I had slept with my parents. Being of Indian origin, I was acutely aware that most of the Eastern world slept with their children. It felt natural. Also, practising as a child protection senior practitioner, I was aware of the concept of attachment and wanted to ensure our attachment was secure. I thought I had one chance to do that and didn't want to compromise and blow it!

Dalvinder, mother of Amber, five, India, three, and Jasmine, 11 months 🔊🔊

Sound good? Then you might like the methods of Dr William Sears, Sheila Kitzinger, Dr Benjamin Spock, Elizabeth Pantley and Dr James McKenna.

By the Clock

Structured routine and doting discipline

The By the Clock approach is great for anyone who thrives on routine, structure and good timekeeping! It centres on helping your baby learn to settle herself. It appeals to parents – and babies – who like to know what to expect. It particularly suits one-child families where other obligations can be tailored to the needs of the child. It also suits those with extra childcare – such as a nanny – on hand to help shoe-horn family life into the routine. It might not suit families whose routines fluctuate, people who need spontaneity or those who feel restricted by a timetable.

🔊🔊 With Sara, who's now two, we were quite 'go with the flow' but you can be when you've only got one child. When we knew Phoebe was coming, we decided we'd definitely go with a structured routine. She's two months now, and already she's slept through the night several times. And it's the only thing saving my sanity! We're even going to start to ease Sara into a similar routine, even though it's late in the day for her.

Gemma, mother of Sara, two, and Phoebe, two months

99

Sound good? Then you might like the methods of Dr Richard Ferber, Gina Ford, Jodi Mindell, Tracy Hogg (The Baby Whisperer) and Dr Marc Weissbluth.

Flexi-Sleeping

For babies with older siblings, or for working parents and those who want to go with the flow.

The Flexi-Sleeping approach is highly suitable for parents and babies with other people to consider, for example, older siblings with hectic social lives. It suits families with lots of commitments, or with frequently changing routines, locations and demands and for parents who like their children to be adaptable and open to a loose routine. It can be a lifesaver for parents who have their own working routines to consider – such as mums who need to work from home during nap times, or parents who want to spend time in the early evening with a baby they haven't seen all day. It might not suit those who need to know they will get certain windows of guaranteed peace all day, or those who want a short day for their baby with an early-as-possible bedtime.

Sound good? Then you might like the methods of Dr Sears, The Baby Whisperer, Sheila Kitzinger and Dreena Hamilton.

Multiple Madness

Sleep solutions for twins, triplets or more

The Multiple Madness approach has practical solutions for larger families. What do you do when it's not just one little person to get to sleep? How do you prevent them keeping each other – and you – awake all night? This approach is the strategy for families with twins and multiples, and can also appeal to families with children with little age difference.

> **"** When we found out we were having twins, all our plans flew out of the window. When they were born, we were lucky just to keep putting one foot in front of the other. But we did stumble into a few good twin tips along the way — it is possible to have twins in a routine. In fact, we think it's pretty much essential.
>
> Matt, father of Luke and Perry, seven **"**

Sound good? Then you might like the methods of Dr Marc Weissbluth, Gina Ford, The Baby Whisperer, Ruth Cockburn.

REAL-LIFE AND EXPERT ADVICE

In addition to a discussion of the four approaches in each chapter, you will also find tips, advice and accounts of experiences from parents who have tried it all.

Each chapter also has tips and advice from Baby Sleep expert Sara Warren. Sara began training as a midwife in the USA where she was a doula and childbirth educator. She completed her training in the UK and worked as a registered midwife before going on to work in public health, specialising in giving up smoking in pregnancy. She has also worked for *midwives online*, and has accrued a fair bit of personal hands-on experience from birthing and raising her own six children.

But remember, nobody's telling you how you *must* do it. Use this book as a resource – but trust your instincts. Sleep is not lost forever to you... you just need a map. And the route you choose to follow is up to you.

> Note from the author: You will notice that throughout the book the baby is referred to as 'she'. This is for consistency and ease of reading only.

1

Coming Home

" People who say they sleep like a baby usually don't have one.'

Leo J Burke

They say tiny newborns only do three things – eat, poo and sleep – so by the time you bring your baby home, there are probably only three main decisions you will already have had to either make or give some serious thought to: how to feed her (breast or bottle), what kind of nappies to use (cloth or disposable) and where she will sleep (options rather less straightforward).

I heard a woman say once that discussing babies' sleep arrangements is akin to discussion religion and politics: you just don't do it, because it is too laden with emotion and the fear of being judged.

However, this attitude is best got rid off. Because what's right for your baby may not be right for mine, and vice versa. Only a baby's parents can know what works for that baby and that family. So go with your instinct, the one you felt was probably right way back when you were first pregnant, and then go for it.

Where your baby sleeps

Some parents will have firm views from early on in pregnancy on the sleeping arrangements their new family will adopt. I have friends who were certain from day one that baby would be in a room of her own from the earliest possible opportunity and others who knew that they couldn't survive a single night with the baby sleeping more than six inches away from them.

Most of us are more ambivalent (or confused) and take a kind of scattergun approach.

For instance, before my daughter was born (and indeed my son, even though I'd already been through it once already) we had, by the time she came home, fully decorated a small nursery for her, complete with a cot made up with sheets and ready to go, and a breastfeeding chair on stand-by. But we also had a Moses basket at the ready by my side of the bed, equally primed for action with even smaller little sheets and cellular blankets. It turned out that Evie occupied the Moses basket for three months, but being what the midwives described as a 'long baby', soon found her toes pressing on the ends and made the move to her cot at that point. When she did, I felt a curious mixture of sadness that she was no longer at arm's reach and relief that I could turn over, cough and get up to go to the loo in the night without waking her up.

> We were a bit confused about where Nick should sleep. My natural instinct was to have him as close as possible to me, but we knew very soon we would want our own space back, and planned to move him into his own room quite early on.
>
> It's such a personal decision, I don't think anyone can tell you what's going to be right for you, as a couple and as parents.

Sarah, mother of Nicholas, six months

Choosing a 'Coming Home' approach

- Know yourselves. Do you, as parents, fall broadly into the camp that thinks the so-called 'cry-it-out' method, which says you should put a baby to bed awake and let her fuss until she falls asleep (with limits on how long she should cry and how often you should comfort her)? Or are you in the 'no tears' camp, which believes generally that you should comfort a baby as soon as she cries, because she knows her own needs and will fall into a routine if she feels secure? Once you have figured this out, you can then opt for a specific method. This book offers four approaches, and also suggests particular 'gurus', experts and authors whose methods fall broadly within these approaches, so you can follow up with similar opinions.

- Once you have chosen, be consistent. This is the key – all the family must be on board, and switching often between conflicting parts of various methods will just confuse you and your baby. Think of sleep training as being split into two parts – teaching your baby to fall asleep at bedtime, and teaching her to fall back to sleep if she wakes up during the night. Try to use the same approach for both parts. But also try to be flexible – if you have chosen a method that just doesn't feel right once you have started, allow yourself to have a go at something else.

- Be mindful of your baby's age. For the first three months, most experts agree that training your baby to sleep may not be appropriate because she is usually feeding round the clock. By about six weeks, you may start teaching your baby the difference between night and day, and as she gives up night feeds, you will find a routine is easier to maintain. Some methods, however, especially those that fit into the By the Clock category, aim to get baby into some kind of routine from Day One.

- Don't despair if a method that worked for your friend doesn't work for you. Every baby is different. Try not to compare yours with other people's, and don't worry about deviating from a method when common sense tells you to. These approaches are just that: helpful approaches, not straitjackets. Think of it like a favourite family recipe – you follow the essentials, but each member of the family adds little ingredients and touches of their own.

Now have a look at the *Baby Sleep Bible* approaches you can come home to – and find out how to set them up.

BACK TO NATURE

The method

You will find many buzzwords if you start to look into the so-called 'natural' approach to baby sleep. 'Attachment parenting', 'co-sleeping', 'the family bed', 'shared sleep', 'the no-cry approach' – all of these, while differing a little in their origins and exact methods, broadly embrace the notion that babies sleep better – and usually mothers, especially breastfeeding ones, too – if they are in your room with you rather than in a room or cot of their own.

Although these methods have been becoming increasingly popular in Western countries only in recent years, this is not a new concept. Until the 19th century it was common in the UK too – the advantage being that a shared bed meant shared warmth.

Co-sleeping is standard practice in many areas of the world, and in some countries such as India it is the norm.

In the Victorian era, the practice of sharing a bed with children became less common, but recently practitioners of attachment parenting, most notably American paediatrician Dr William Sears, have reintroduced the idea into Western culture and it is gaining ground. Proponents maintain that co-sleeping promotes bonding, helps mothers to breastfeed, makes bottle-feeding easier, enables parents to get more sleep, and may protect against sudden infant death syndrome (SIDS) because a baby sleeping next to her mother is more likely to be heard if she is in distress or if she is having breathing problems.

The approach, though, is not without controversy. Some critics believe co-sleeping with a baby *increases* the risk of SIDS, and some governments, including the British government, advise parents not to co-sleep, especially during the first six months. Some believe there is a danger of a small infant being crushed or smothered, and some stress that a premature or ill baby, whose risk of SIDS is already increased, shouldn't co-sleep. Others say the practice promotes an unhealthy dependence of the child on the parent, as well as interfering with intimacy between the parents. Some also believe that breastfeeding babies wake up more often to feed, and because they can smell their mother's milk, often develop the habit of waking to feed long after they physically need to, making it harder to wean them.

So, as you will find with all approaches, it's a case of balancing out the advice.

Who does it suit?

The Back to Nature approach will probably suit you if you like the idea of night-time bonding and don't panic at the thought of not being able to sink into your bed and toss and turn in a thick duvet with abandon. If you are planning to breastfeed, there is much to be said for being able to turn to your baby in the night and feed without getting up, and if you nod off during the breastfeeding, it doesn't matter – in fact, some clever mums say they are almost able to complete a whole night-time feed in their sleep. Also, it stands to reason that if a small baby feeds at night and, when finished, is tucked up warm and drowsy and close to mum, she will probably drop back off to sleep faster than a baby who has to be re-settled in a cot.

> **"** After having Caesareans both times I found it useful to co-sleep with the baby as I was breastfeeding and found that I could just roll the baby across me into the correct position instead of having to bend or sit up.
>
> I feel that by choosing to co-sleep initially, I slept a lot more and the baby was more content and I would do it that way again (I stopped co-sleeping both times by about 6 weeks).
>
> Lisa, a midwife and mother of Fionn, three, and Bridget, 10 months **"**

Putting it into practice

If you decide that you would like to try co-sleeping when you bring your baby home from the hospital, what can you do to prepare in advance? Probably the biggest considerations have to do with safety.

Although researchers have actually found that more babies die alone in cots or on sofas than in 'family beds', the most significant risks associated with co-sleeping have to do with unsuitable and unsafe bedding, and in particular with babies sleeping next to adults who have been smoking, taking drugs or drinking alcohol, or who are on medications that may cause drowsiness or deep sleep. With this in mind, there are lots of things you can do to make extra sure that your baby is safe in your bed or bedroom. And, if you are on the fence about this, and considering a 'family bed' in the true sense of the word with some trepidation – pictures of an unidentified jumble of limbs and tousled heads, and an ever-widening gulf of physical distance between you and your partner – remember that there are *degrees* of co-sleeping.

So if you want to sleep share but feel the need for some safety reassurance, there are several products that can help:

- 'Sidecar' cots or bassinets that attach to the side of the adult bed, which have barriers on three sides but are open to the parent's side, creating a kind of 'baby annex' so your baby has her own space and you have yours, but she is at a finger's reach and is easy to reach when it's time to feed.

- Bed-top 'wedges' which sit next to you on the bed and have raised curved sides to prevent your baby rolling off. These usually have the added advantage of absorbing breast milk, dribble and other night-time leakages.

- Side rails to prevent your baby rolling off the bed.

- Baby 'enclosures' or 'nests', which are placed onto the adult mattress.

If you would like a looser form of sleep sharing, but not all in the same bed, you could consider:

- 'Dual beds', where the mother has one place where she sleeps with the baby, and another where she sleeps with her partner, moving back and forth according to how often the baby wakes up and how tired she feels

- 'Musical beds', where there are several different beds in different rooms, and parents and baby move from place to place according to any given evening's requirements

- 'Occasional family bed', where the baby has her own crib or cot, but is welcomed into the parents' bed if she is poorly or unsettled, or for extra bonding

- Or simply a Moses basket placed directly next to the bed – but because most baskets on stands are level with bed height and small enough to manoeuvre next to the bed means that this is a good half-way house option, and baby is still at arm's reach.

If you prefer to go with a standard adult bed arrangement, though, you could consider:

- Using a king-sized bed if possible, or if not, a queen-sized one. Some parents put a second single mattress next to their own, but it is essential to ensure there is no gap between the beds or mattresses, and that the baby cannot fall or get trapped between the beds or between a bed and a wall. Wedge rolled-up towels into any gaps. Also check for gaps of more than $2^3/_8$ inches (about the diameter of a can of fizzy drink) or cut-outs in the headboard that the baby could get stuck in.

- Putting the mattress directly on the floor – there is less room to fall.

- Using a firm mattress (but not a waterbed or eggbox-style mattress) – a firm mattress carries less risk of suffocation.

- Substituting duvets for traditional sheets and blankets, which can be removed in layers to prevent overheating and are less likely to end up over the baby's head.

> 66 I wanted us to do co-sleeping because I was breastfeeding and found it was less disruptive in the night if the baby was right there next to me. But a friend told me to make sure we put Jake in his own cot by the time he was one, because otherwise it gets very hard to get them out of your bed later.
>
> Carrie, mother of Jake, 14 months 99

Once you have decided on the actual bed arrangement, you will need to think about the following safety issues:

- Keep the baby's head clear of loose bedding or comforters, and don't use a pillow or sheepskin covers for the baby.

- Put the baby on their back to sleep, as you would in a cot or Moses basket.

- Don't put a baby together with an older infant or toddler in a bed in your room. The baby should be with you, and not next to an older child for at least the first six months.

- If using fitted sheets, make sure they cannot be pulled loose.

- If using a low mattress that your baby will be left alone on for naps, childproof the room – you never know when she will decide to crawl!

- Place rugs or pillows on the floor around the mattress or bed to cushion falls. If using a rail on a bed, you could use a mesh one that won't trap heads or limbs.

- Position the bed away from hazards such as window blind cords, lamps and heavy objects which could be pulled over.

- The safest place in the bed is between the mother and the wall or guard rail, rather than in between two parents. Research has shown that mothers have a more finely tuned instinctual awareness of the baby's location and state of sleep.

- If you have been drinking alcohol, smoking, using drugs or medications, are a very deep sleeper or are very overweight, it is recommended that you don't co-sleep. It is safer to put your baby in a crib next to you. If you have simply had a boozy night out, use the crib temporarily – co-sleeping doesn't have to be an all-or-nothing approach.

- It is better to use fewer covers and blankets but instead dress yourself and the baby warmly for sleep – clothes don't ride up and suffocate. Bear in mind your collective body warmth will increase through the night though – so avoid thick jumpers.

- Don't swaddle a baby if you are co-sleeping, because they are likely to feel warmer anyway due to shared body heat, and tight swaddling can prevent a baby from wriggling free and cooling down.

- Don't wear nightclothes with long ribbons that could choke your baby. Also, don't wear jewellery, tie back long hair and don't wear strong perfumes.

- Don't leave your baby alone in the bed. During the early evening or for short naps, start the baby in a crib or Moses basket, and let them join you when you are ready to sleep.

- Keep pets away from the bed.

> It's never a good idea to share a family bed if one or both parents smoke, even if they go outside to smoke. The reason for this is that carbon monoxide and other chemicals in cigarette smoke are exhaled on the breath for several hours after smoking and these gases could be trapped and concentrated under and around bedding making it easier for the baby to inhale. In fact smoking is a leading cause of SIDS, making this the perfect time to contact local stop smoking services for advice and help to quit if ready.'
>
> Sara Warren, midwife

Remember that co-sleeping is a family choice, and should be a family decision.

Talk to your partner. And pre-empt intimacy issues by planning some time alone with them rather than hoping it will just happen. (This can be a fun, novel way of injecting life into your physical relationship.) Also, don't feel restricted by your decision. Some babies seem only to sleep when in the bed with a parent, others seem to need the solitude of their own sleeping place. Be flexible – you will have to wait and see what kind of baby you get!

> **❝** My husband was very against having a baby in our bed. Luckily our bed is queen sized. Once he got used to it and realised Amber would not die, he did have to admit his sleep was rarely disrupted as Amber and I were so in tune that we woke together and I would feed her with no fuss. It must have worked because I have done the same for all three of our children!
>
> Dalvinder, mother of Amber, five, India, three, and Jasmine, 11 months **❞**

BY THE CLOCK

The method

If the lure of a set bedtime and a quiet evening shines like a beacon through the mists of the early baby days, then you might consider a structured parenting, By the Clock approach. However, like the Back to Nature approach, this approach – which is inspired by a range of techniques from the routines advocated by Gina Ford to the cry-it-out sleep training of Dr Richard Ferber – is also not without its share of controversy.

The structured approach is a relatively new (as in the past century and a half or so) idea about how to get a baby to sleep.

Parents in the industrialised world found the promise of helping a baby to go to sleep quickly, easily and for long periods of time very attractive. The various guru-led methods which might come under this heading are usually proponents of a set bedtime routine, establishing good associations with sleep, bedtime and the nursery, and often with using a 'progressive waiting', 'cry-it-out' or 'controlled crying' strategy where the baby is put to bed awake and the parent leaves the room for short, but progressively longer stretches of time until the baby falls asleep.

Who does it suit?

Proponents of these kinds of methods firmly believe that babies – and indeed older children – need reassuring routines and boundaries in order to feel secure.

They say that giving a baby a set routine where they know exactly what's coming up next gives them the ability to get themselves to sleep calmly and peacefully, and also promotes a healthy independence from their mother, which is necessary to grow and develop. Many parents also find routine-based approaches a God-send if they are dealing with troubled children, or twins or multiples, or simply large families. Others find the detailed routines of gurus such as Gina Ford overly restrictive, leaving little time for spontaneity or for unplanned events. And critics of so-called 'Ferberisation' – or following Dr Ferber's methods – even go so far as to brand them cruel or neglectful – although Ferber himself stresses that his methods are designed specifically to avoid crying and that he does not approve of leaving a crying baby alone for long periods.

> 66 Our first, Heather, was a textbook 'Gina baby' and slept 7pm – 7am from six weeks old. I liked the prescriptive nature of a routine-based method. Routine is the key, and we stuck with that to the letter every night, same time, same everything. But our second, Murray, didn't think much of it though, and we just went with the flow when we realised we weren't going to win with him.

Caroline, mother of Heather, five, and
Murray, two 99

Putting it into practice

Where do you start if you feel a By the Clock approach might be for you – but you want to make sure your baby will feel loved and nurtured, and have that crucial time to bond with you and the rest of your family?

Firstly, it is important to stress that even Dr Ferber himself does not advocate using cry-it-out methods before the age of six months, and certainly not before four months. Methods such as Ford's can be used from Day One, but build up gently into a routine suitable for each age stage.

So there's no need to worry that the warm fuggy bubble you existed in with your baby in those first days after birth will be cruelly popped by having to instigate a strict routine in the early days.

How to use such methods to encourage your baby to sleep through the night will be covered in the next chapter. However, you will need to set in motion a few gentle steps that will pave the way to this approach later on. Firstly, set up the sleeping arrangements:

- In the UK, and in America, we are advised that infants sleep in the same room as their parents for the first six months to reduce the risk of SIDS and to facilitate breastfeeding. You can do this while preparing your baby for her own 'space' by having the baby sleep in a Moses basket next to you, or in a wooden crib, or even the 'sidecar' cot arrangement (where the cot has three sides but leaves one side open to your bed) that also works for co-sleeping.

- If you do decide to put your baby straight into a room of her own, it is better if it is the room next to yours. You could also consider a video monitor, and possibly also a baby mat alarm, where the baby sleeps on a thin sensor mat under the sheet, and an alarm goes off if her breathing or movement stops.

- Even if you plan to have your baby in your room at first, have their nursery ready by birth. Take the baby in there for naps, baths, storytime and cuddles. By the time you want her to transfer to her own room, she will see it as a comforting and familiar place.

- Buy a full-size cot even if your baby will be in a Moses basket or crib – let her have odd naps in the cot so the transition when she outgrow the smaller crib will be easier.

- Have all your cot, crib or Moses basket bedding washed and ready to go before the birth – you will find routines easier to get into if you are calm and prepared.

- Put blackout linings on curtains, or even better, use blackout blinds.

- Find room for a chair – preferably a comfy breastfeeding one but if space is tight just a small high-back one – because when your baby sleeps in her own room, you need somewhere for cuddles and feeding and stories. If you can't sit down, you will spend less time loving and bonding in her special space.

> **"** If you plan it from Day One, it's a lot easier. We had the nursery set up with blackout blinds and the cot all made up with sheets, even though Stanley, and later Poppy, slept in a Moses basket in our room for the first six months. But Gill would put them down for daytime naps in their big cot, and use the chair for storytimes and cuddles. By the time they made the move, it was a natural progression.
>
> Alex, father of Stanley, four, and Poppy,
> 19 months **"**

Secondly, start to introduce the idea of a routine. Try to:

- Keep visitors to a minimum during your first week home – a calm start will help you find your baby's own rhythms.

- Instigate from the beginning a good bedtime routine – even if your baby doesn't have a set single 'bedtime' yet, create one in the early evening before one of her due naps. However tiny your baby is, she will still respond to a gentle bath, a feed, a nursery rhyme or short story or lullaby in a dimly lit room and a cuddle before being laid down in the dark.

- Slowly introduce other 'daily habits', such as a walk in the pram or buggy after lunch. The Baby Whisperer, the late Tracy

Hogg, recommended a routine that sets up the idea of 'eat – play – sleep' in sequence throughout the day, and which can be adapted for younger babies right through to toddlers. Likewise, Ford's techniques grow with your child from Day One to toddlers and older children. Try to keep your baby awake for a short time after every feed, and play with and stimulate her for a while before she naps.

> **"** If you have three or more children, you've got to have some kind of order, or you'd go mad. The only thing that kept us going was knowing we'd have a relatively calm and grown-up evening.
>
> Tom, father of Rebecca, eight, Ashley, five, and Vincent, three **"**

By the age of three months, you will begin to see your baby settle into a good routine. Between this age and around six months, they will be physically ready to sleep through the night – although Ford says her methods will have babies sleeping from 7pm to 7am from an impressive eight to 12 weeks.

The trick to implementing any By the Clock method is to keep everything calm, measured and loving – be assured that a routine-loving parent isn't cold or unnatural.

Most By the Clock babies thrive on a structured approach, and if the baby is happy and secure, then the parents and the rest of the family will probably be happy and rested too.

However, By the Clock isn't a literal label – you can introduce routine and structure into your life in a range of degrees. In other words, you don't have to watch the second hand ticking throughout the day, waiting for your 'time' to move on to the next slot in your schedule. You can make it as rigid or as flexible as you choose. And neither does By the Clock mean that your baby is somehow less cherished or nurtured than a co-sleeping baby. In fact, if parents feel happy and confident and well-rested, there's a good chance that they will have more time and enthusiasm for all those lovely cosy moments of bonding that they had imagined before the birth. In even the most rigid of routines, there is always, always plenty of time for cuddles.

FLEXI-SLEEPING

The method

The first thing to say about Flexi-Sleeping is that flexible doesn't mean chaotic. Flexi-Sleeping is all about finding an approach to your baby's sleep which has a routine of some kind, but is able to shift and react to changing locations, or circumstances, or the demands of the other adults and siblings in the family.

It's all about providing a few aspects in your baby's routine and daily life which remain more or less predictable, and which then allow your baby to feel secure despite an otherwise fluctuating set of circumstances, carers or locations.

66 I have always been sceptical about following the 'gurus', believing that you have to find your own routine. Common sense and your own instincts as a mum were more important to me.

Maxine, mother of Marnie, 10, and
Freddy, four 99

Who does it suit?

If there is one *Baby Sleep Bible* approach which should appeal to the 'been there, done that' parent, it's Flexi-Sleeping. It should also suit working parents, parents of twins or multiples, parents with large families, parents with demanding or unusual working hours, and parents who think they are something of a free spirit.

- 'I'd love to follow a structured approach and time every feed and nap to the minute, but it's just impossible when I have two other children.'

- 'I really like the idea of the Family Bed, but I'm not sure how it would work because my husband does shifts, and I sometimes have to be away one night a week for work.'

- 'My husband and I separated while I was pregnant. He wants eventually to have Keisha at weekends, or maybe even a few nights a week. How can we work together to find a way of establishing a sleep routine for her that will fit in to both of our lives?'

- 'I will have to go back to work full-time when my son is eight months. He'll be going to a day nursery. So what's the point of getting him into a routine, when the nursery will just impose its own different routine on him then?'

- 'I've never been very organised. The idea of sticking to a timetable scares me silly! But equally, I'm not really the 'earth mother' type, and don't think I could cope with co-sleeping. Is it damaging to just 'go with the flow' and let my baby sleep in the buggy or the car whenever he nods off?'

- 'My daughter has just started three days a week with a childminder. The childminder is willing to give my routine a go, but she says it won't always fit in with the other children. I feel like everything I've set up for my daughter will be ruined.'

- 'My husband doesn't get home from work until an hour later than my routine says I should put our baby to bed. How can I keep my baby up a bit to see him but not destroy bedtime?'

Do any of the above scenarios strike a chord? There is a strong likelihood that one or other of them might – because this is life. Life with other children, other adults, outside factors; life that doesn't always go to plan, or follow the same plan every day.

> 66 I can see why some people do a routine-based method, but it would have been impossible for me because of having to take him everywhere with me. George would sleep wherever we went, he was so relaxed about it all. If his routine went out of kilter by half an hour or something, it didn't bother him.
>
> Nikki, childminder and mother of George, six 99

It's easy to feel – first-time parent or 'been there, done that' parent – that if your parenting and your baby don't fit neatly into a recognised little pigeon hole, there must be something somehow substandard or disorganised about you. And if this is how you feel, you are probably in the majority. Which is why Flexi-Sleeping could help.

Putting it into practice

Flexi-Sleeping means keeping a kind of thin but strong 'chain of constants' throughout your day and your child's routine, which will provide a kind of backbone for the rest of the day – however it turns out – to hang on.

By providing these constants, you are giving your baby fixed points of security – remember how babies like to know what to expect – which don't change despite other changes in location, or timing or people. What is remarkable about this approach is that it can bend towards elements of either Back to Nature or By the Clock, so that you get to follow the techniques you want even if circumstances seem at first to make them impossible. You can still look at the methods of, for instance, Dr Sears, Dreena Hamilton, Sheila Kitzinger or Tracy Hogg – you just have to 'pin' their basic approach onto those certain fixed points to make them achievable.

So, for instance, if you want to co-sleep, but you work some nights, could you put your baby on a mattress next to you that night instead of in your bed, so that you don't disturb each other, and so that Dad can sleep next to baby until you get in?

Or, if you would like to try a By the Clock routine but your childminder feels it will be too restrictive, can you work out together a few basic rules that she will adhere to, such as keeping your baby awake for a play after a feed, so that your home routine won't be compromised?

Here are some good ways in which you can prepare for coming home to a Flexi-Sleeping approach:

- Before the birth, buy a few Flexi-Sleeping essentials:
  - Three cellular blankets, all the same colour
  - Three identical sets of pyjamas or sleepsuits
  - Three baby sleeping bags in the same design
  - A clip-on musical lullaby player/nightlight
  - A baby book containing a selection of short rhymes or lullabies
  - A blankie or taggie blanket or cuddle toy, preferably in duplicate, and suitable from birth
  - A soft, 'plush' design photo holder or photo cube with plastic inserts designed to be safe for a baby

- Decide which broad approach you would have liked to follow if current circumstances were not a factor – a co-sleeping approach? A firm routine?

- Make a list of the 'significant others' who will be part of your baby's daily routine. Arrange a time you can sit down with them and tell them what you will be doing at home, and find ways together to fit their time away from you into that approach.

Draw up an informal 'agreement' with that person. It might be very simple: 'Amy will have naps in her cot in a dark room at 10am and 2pm. Before she goes to sleep, she will have a chance to play and then a story.' Or it might, if the other person is willing, be a full routine detailing food, naps and activities from start to finish. Put in a clause: 'I realise that you might sometimes have to do things differently, and that's ok. I appreciate any efforts you can make to help me establish Amy's routine.' Then offer to provide, or contribute to, any equipment or furniture which will make it easier for the other person to follow your approach. This might be an extra mattress for a separated partner's home, for example, if he's going to co-sleep when your baby visits him. Or blackout blinds for Granny's house, or books to keep at the childminder's house, or an extra Moses basket.

> **"** We use the same sheets and curtains and nightlight at our house and at my mother's house, where he stays quite often. Mum also has a few 'duplicate' favourite bedtime books. I'm sure it helps Mason settle.
>
> Jon, father of Mason, three **"**

Once baby is home, you can then start to put together your 'chain of constants'. It's all about making your baby recognise and feel safe with a few key distinctive objects, habits and sounds which are linked to sleep:

- In the early days, when your baby might be in a Moses basket or a crib, or in the bed with you, try to *always* put them in the same coloured sleepsuit or pyjamas, and cover them with the same coloured cellular blanket.

- When they are older, you might choose to swap to a baby sleeping bag – these are fantastic. They don't fall off or ride up, they provide a familiar cosy bedtime comfort (in fact we always call them 'cosies' in our house), and older babies find it harder to climb out of cots when they're wearing them!

- When your baby goes to sleep, give them their cuddly toy or blankie – somewhere between six months and a year they usually latch on to one that's been in the cot constantly.

- Put photos of you, your partner and any siblings in the photo holder and place it within sight of where your baby sleeps.

- At *every* nap time and bedtime, try to sit down near to where they will be sleeping, and read or sing them a rhyme or lullaby from their 'bedtime book'.

- Then play the musical lullaby player, turn out the light, and lay your baby down to sleep (or cuddle up with them if you are co-sleeping).

- If the nap is out in the buggy, or in the car, still cover them with the same coloured cellular blanket (you could keep one in the car so it's always to hand), give them their comforter, and perhaps sing one of the familiar lullabies.

All of these steps are a good idea under any approach, and will instil good associations with sleep times.

If you follow these steps from Day One and continue to do so over the first weeks and months, you will soon find that your baby has internalised these 'constants', and you can then begin to transfer them to their 'other places' or use them when a sudden change of location or timing occurs.

Here are some examples.

You want to keep structured naps but fit them in around after-school activities for older siblings

Take your blankets, book, comforter, even musical player (you can get quite small portable ones) and baby sleeping bag (you can buy these with slits in for the reins in buggies and car seats). When your older child has gone into a class, go through your usual routine in the buggy or car. Even if your baby doesn't initially fall asleep, the routine will be relaxing and comforting.

You want to co-sleep but you and your partner sometimes work at night

As long as one of you is there, and baby is dressed in her familiar night-time clothes and follows her familiar routine, there shouldn't be any problem.

Your children have to sleep sometimes at grandma's house or at the childminder

Take familiar objects, especially the photo holder with your baby, and ask granny or the childminder to follow your bedtime sequence. The familiarity of the routine and the objects will make it easier for your baby to accept a different carer and location. And if the childminder has to deviate from timings due to the other children, the familiar objects will help relax your baby if she was over-tired or had missed a nap.

> My mum looks after Nicholas twice a week and I was worried that this would unsettle his sleeping patterns. It worked out fine though, after I explained the routine I had been using. Although she had never followed a routine with any of her

> own children, she's embraced it and Nick seems to be sleeping well at grandma's too!
>
> Sarah, mother of Nicholas, six months **99**

You need to fit in with a parent who is separated from you and lives elsewhere

Try to duplicate your list of 'Flexi-Sleeping essentials' so the routine can be carried out the same but without having to constantly transport equipment.

> **66** I drew up a little plan for Sasha's dad, so he knew roughly what her day was about. We are also quite careful about keeping to a similar bedtime routine, and Sasha has a little album of photos of both of us, so she can look at either of us if we're not there.
>
> Kim, mother of Sasha, two **99**

You need to put your baby in a day nursery

Even the strictest of nurseries should be willing to work with you on things that don't disturb the other children, such as a blanket or a baby sleeping bag or a lullaby. If they won't listen at all or dismiss you out of hand, try to find another nursery – this inflexibility will extend to your baby's total experience there.

You hate routine and want your baby to 'go with the flow' and sleep on the move

Simply adding in these essential 'constants' will enable you to be really flexible and take your baby out and about with you, but still give her that sense of security and safety that she needs.

A secure baby will actually adapt to different situations more willingly than a baby who feels unsure and on edge.

You want to keep baby up slightly later in the evening so that your partner can see her during the week
Add in an extra daytime nap time, and extend the 'bedtime period' with a longer story and lullaby time. If you stick to this modified routine, your baby will still keep a daily rhythm.

Flexi-Sleeping doesn't need a lot of time or money to set up – just a bit of thought.

Even adventurous adults like certain things around them to be constant – a favourite pair of slippers, a morning routine of coffee and a croissant, a certain radio station on the way to work. Giving your baby their own constants will set her up to be a confident sleeper, wherever she lays her head.

MULTIPLE MADNESS

The method

Many of the parents of multiples I have met have looked at me in incredulity when I have asked which routine they followed. 'Routine? No. *Survival*. Survival is all that matters.' Others have told me with a grim nod that indeed, strict adherence to a structured routine such as Gina Ford was the *only* way they could possibly have got through the months of sleep deprivation.

This method aims to give you an approach to sleep with multiples that can be adapted to either approach.

Who does it suit?

What Multiple Madness aims to do is provide a basis from which parents of multiples can achieve sleep nirvana – and even factor in their own preferences for co-sleeping or routine-based approaches along the way. And if parents of babies who are not twins or multiples, but who are close in age or maybe sharing a bedroom, would like to sneak in and adopt some of this approach, there is plenty that will help single children too.

You need to be aware that the very first approach you choose to take with multiples may be out of your hands.

Hospitals tend to have a standard practice when it comes to putting newborn multiples in separate cribs, or together in the same crib. Co-bedding of multiples, particularly premature babies who need to be in the neonatal intensive care unit (NICU), is increasingly common. It used to be thought that swaddling twin babies (comfortably wrapping them in a sheet or swaddling blanket) and placing them side by side on their backs in the same crib would help them sleep and handle stress better, because the close-fitting quarters are what they have been used to in the womb. However, swaddling tends to be discouraged these days, as it has been established that the risk of SIDS is increased with overheating. It's important not to wrap babies so tightly that they can't wriggle out if they are becoming too hot.

If your babies slept together in hospital, though, it may be that you decide to carry on with this – especially if your babies were premature and spent a relatively long time in hospital in that routine. Or you may decide that, on coming home, you will use a different set-up.

Putting it into practice

Much has been written by parents and experts on the best approaches. Ford is a good approach for those who would like a very structured approach – but equally, Sears has advised on how to co-sleep with multiples. See the Introduction for more information.

Here is a good guide to those early days, which takes in both approaches:

Setting up the sleeping arrangements

- Consider loose swaddling, to re-create that cosy womb-like feel – but don't wrap tightly.

  Avoid rocking them to sleep – put them to bed drowsy but awake. They need to be able to settle themselves if one of them wakes the other up in the night.

- If your babies sleep in the same cot, they will comfort each other – some give each other cuddles or even suck on each other's fingers. This is probably fine up to about three months – if you want them to sleep together after that, you can buy double-width twin cots, or L-shaped 'twin sleepers', which later transform into toddler beds, and after that to even a small sofa.

- If you want them to sleep together in the early days but are worried about SIDS – the risk of cot death is slightly higher with twins than with single babies – you might want to buy a special cot divider which cuts across the middle of the cot from side to side, and allows both babies to sleep at their own end of the cot in the feet-to-feet position. These are suitable from birth to around seven months.

- You can also buy twin travel cots for trips to see family, or for holidays, or sleeping at a childminders.

- If you decide to put your babies in separate cribs or cots, make sure they can still see each other.

> **&&** Luke and Perry shared a cot in our room in the early days – they 'topped and tailed', but usually ended up cuddling each other, or with legs and arms entwined. They never seemed to really disturb each other, and it felt like the right thing to do.
>
> Matt, father of Luke and Perry, seven **99**

Starting a routine

- Think about synchronisation. If one baby wakes up, awaken the other so they can both be fed and changed at the same time. This applies to daytime naps and at night. It stops them playing the game of 'twin tag' where one baby wakes up, and by the time you have fed, changed and put her back down, the other one awakes like clockwork ready for his turn. This cycle can go on for hours, leaving no time for you to sleep.

  If you are on your own, leave it 20–25 minutes before waking the second baby, so that you don't have to hold both at once. Twins get used to speed feeding!

- Try to put your babies to sleep at the same time – it may take several weeks, but they will eventually keep to a similar schedule and leave you some time to do other things while they are asleep.

- Try to have the same kind of calming bedtime routine that you would with a single baby – a warm bath, story, cuddle. These are the signals that it is time to sleep.

- Tend to your calm baby first – if one is screaming and the other is calm, you will instinctively want to pick up the loud one. But if you do, your quiet baby will miss out on the attention she needs. Settle the quiet one first, and then comfort the crying baby.

Don't worry that one will wake the other – most multiples don't seem bothered by their sibling's crying.

Other points to consider

- Remember that sleeping schedules with multiples usually go by the babies' weight, not their age, as they are often premature. Try not to compare other babies and be despondent that yours are lagging behind – remember that your babies' birth age might be several weeks different to their 'developmental age'.

- Keep the babies calm and quiet during night-time feeds – keep the room dimly lit, and try not to hold them more than you have to. Feed them and put them straight back down. This will help them learn that nights are for sleeping.

- You can extend this idea by trying 'dream feeding', when you pre-empt your baby waking due to hunger by feeding her while she is still asleep. You can do this with breast or bottle feeding – you baby will instinctively start suckling when she senses a teat or nipple.

- You might want to consider asking for night-time help. Can a granny or close relative stay with you for the first few weeks, and help with night-time feeds? If budgets stretch, could you hire a maternity night nurse? Don't be afraid to accept help – the rest of the world already stands in awe of you, so you have nothing to prove!

> The twins slept one either side of our bed in Moses baskets for the first three months. Having the babies in our room certainly affected our relationship. It took about four months to resume marital relations! Broken sleep equals tiredness equals irritability!
>
> It was hard to settle them both some nights. One would be asleep and the other would be screaming! We had one Moses basket on a wooden stand and the other was part of a three-in-one travel system. Sometimes we literally wheeled the noisy one into the en suite!
>
> Callie, mother of Lily, four, and James and Sophia, two

Co-sleeping with twins or multiples – how to do it safely

You might still need to keep to a routine, but your babies can sleep with you. You will need to think about:

- The bed arrangement – a king-sized bed might be large enough for parents and twins, or you can go for a 'sidecar' crib. Follow the same safety checks that are listed under Back to Nature – make sure there are no gaps or unsafe bedding, and never co-sleep if you are overly tired, on medication, smoke, or have taken drugs or alcohol.

- Place the twins on their backs in the centre of the bed. Use a tightly fitted sheet.

- Dress them in comfortable pyjamas or sleepsuits, warm enough that they will only need a light blanket to keep them warm.

- Keep all the supplies you might need through the night next to the bed – but out of reach of the babies.

- If dad is a heavy sleeper or doesn't feel confident that he will not roll onto the babies, consider a 'sidecar' arrangement, where the babies are over on the other side of the mother.

OVER TO YOU

So now it's up to you to plan how you will come home with your baby and how she will sleep. Remember that even sleep expert Dr Ferber, who in his original 1985 book *Solve Your Child's Sleep Problems* advised parents against co-sleeping, has mellowed on his viewpoint in his 2006 revised version, saying:

> **" ** Children do not grow up insecure just because they sleep alone or with other siblings, away from their parents; and they are not prevented from learning to separate, or from developing their own sense of individuality, simply because they sleep with their parents. Whatever you want to do, whatever you feel comfortable doing, is the right thing to do, as long as it works.
>
> Dr Richard Ferber, *Solve Your Child's Sleep Problems*, 1985 **"**

The trick is finding *what* works! As for other parents, or grandparents, or health professionals, or best-selling 'gurus', or well-meaning bystanders – by all means take on board some of their advice, but the final say is yours, and you know your baby better than anyone.

Coming home should be a joy, and sleep an expectation – trust yourself to make both of these a reality.

❝ We've become quite relaxed about Nick's sleeping arrangements. As long as he is happy, and it's working for us, we tend to try a few things out and take on board what worked best. He's not been a perfect sleeper, but I like to think of it as team work: us working with him to get him off to sleep!

Sarah, mother of Nicholas aged six months ❞

2

Sleeping Through the Night

66 A baby usually wakes up in the wee-wee hours of the morning. **99**

Anonymous

By the time your baby is between three and six months old (slightly earlier if you are a By the Clock person or eager to reclaim your evenings), and showing signs of recognising night from day, you might dare to start wondering whether she will soon sleep through the night. Night-time awakenings for food or comfort might start to reduce, and you would probably have started to develop a routine of sorts – or at least a vague set of habits – based on the approach you decided to come home to.

The big question is: has somebody yet asked you (in slightly smug tones if another parent, or 'get on with it' tones if a grandparent): 'Are they sleeping through the night yet?'

Be warned, if it hasn't happened yet, it soon will do. And it will probably be followed by something along the lines of: 'Little Jamie slept through at eight weeks. Twelve hours straight!' or 'We had you sleeping through like clockwork by three months... parents didn't take any nonsense back in our day...'

Welcome to the first 'biggie' of the 'competitive parent milestones' which you will no doubt encounter from now until your little one reaches graduation day. Weaning, crawling, walking, first words, potty training... as your baby blithely gets on with normal baby development, you might find yourself sucked into that unfortunate game parents play of comparing their offspring's achievements and developmental stages with those of everybody else's children.

So, take that deep breath and remind yourself: all babies are different. You know what your baby needs better than anybody else. And *nobody's* baby is still waking up for feeds six times a night when they are five years old. So none of that competitive stuff really matters.

Remind yourself to keep your expectations realistic.

'Sleeping through the night' might suggest 12 hours of solid snooze to you, but in 'doctor-speak' it is far less: doctors consider that a baby is sleeping through the night when they are managing just six hours of uninterrupted sleep. Start small – and remember it will get better!

BACK TO NATURE

The challenges

Some parents might tell you that babies who co-sleep are much more likely to sleep through the night, as they are less likely to wake up stressed or frightened, and more likely to drift back off to sleep without crying if they are cosily tucked up next to mum and her relaxing hormones. Confusingly, others might tell you that co-sleeping with a baby prolongs that period where a baby wakes up regularly during the night to feed, because babies can smell the milk and therefore keep demanding it after they really need it. These people might also tell you that the sheer proximity of another human being to a baby, with all the movement and noise disruption that entails, means that they are unlikely to really sleep through the night until they make the move into their own quarters – and maybe not until they are three or four years old.

But don't despair. Even if your baby is determined to wake you with fidgety cuddles and demands for food (and that's quite apart from sturdy little limbs poking you in your ribs), there are some things you can do to help her ease into proper night-long sleeping.

> **"** We set up our 'family bed' quite late on when Lola was six months old, and was waking up screaming about five or six times a night. We finally thought we'd give it a go, moved her into our bed and she slept peacefully from day one. She'd often still wake up to nurse, but we were all getting a lot more sleep. Co-sleeping isn't for everyone, but it's been the right thing for our family. In fact, when she eventually wants her own 'big girl bed', we'll miss her!
>
> Jane, mother of Lola, nine months **"**

What to do

The first thing to do is relax. It might seem an odd suggestion, but research has shown that mothers sleep differently when they are co-sleeping with a small baby. They are on a kind of 'Mum Alert', where sleep is shallow, and their instincts are tuned into her baby's movements and breathing. Co-sleeping experts who say SIDS is less common in co-sleeping babies also say this is one of the main reasons for the reduction in risk – mum is acting as a permanently switched-on baby alarm through the night.

You might imagine that if your baby is right next to you, you'd feel more reassured and therefore more likely to sleep deeply yourself – but in fact, you will have become used to semi-consciously checking your baby frequently through the night. Even when they start sleeping for longer stretches, you may find you are still sleeping patchily, because you are still 'on duty'.

Do try to learn to find other ways of feeling confident that your baby is safe while you sleep. If you are worried about movement, rolling off the bed, or crushing, maybe buy a 'wedge' if you haven't already. Or consider a move from the main bed to a 'sidecar' or separate mattress. Another idea, if you can face seeing footage of yourself snoring, is to set up your video camera to record your bed for a few hours one night. When you watch it back, you will be able to see that you, your baby (and partner) are actually sleeping safely with each other, and that nothing bad is happening while you are asleep.

Once you reassure yourself that all is well, you will find yourself able to 'let go' and you will have taken your first step towards helping your baby sleep through the night.

The second step you can take is to make your bedroom as conducive to sleep as a baby's nursery would be. Often parents spend many hours preparing a nursery, equipping it with soft furnishings and comforting night lights and calm decor, in order to make it a calm place to rest – and then decide on co-sleeping but completely forget to make their own bedroom baby-friendly.

Adult bedrooms these days are often more than just somewhere to sleep. We might have televisions in there, for instance – or even sometimes a 'home office corner' if pressed for space. Lights might be brighter, and the atmosphere more stimulating. The bedroom can also be too dry and stuffy, or cluttered with clothes.

If you want your baby to sleep through the night in your room, you will have to see it through their eyes, feel it with their senses.

So try to use your bedroom mainly for sleep. If you can, remove anything that is meant for other activities to another room. If you can't do this, can you 'block out' one area – perhaps with a temporary screen? Preferably decorate the room in a neutral and calming colour, and try to let some fresh air in every day.

Here are some other things you can do to make your bedroom more Baby Sleep-friendly:

- Get rid of as many artificial and toxic materials as you can – natural materials and soft textures may be better for your baby.

- Try using blackout blinds, and put a dimmer switch on your ceiling light so that night-time awakenings can be in a soft muted light.

- Try using lamps with low-wattage bulbs that you can reach from your bed.

- If possible, position your bed diagonally across from the door – this is more calming. According to Feng Shui practitioners, if the bed has to be in line with the door, put a wind chime between the two, and a mirror in line with the entrance.

- You can reduce the disturbance factor of any night-time awakenings or feeds by keeping necessary baby gear close by. Keep a changing mat next to the bed, and a packet of wipes and some antibacterial hand gel nearby so you don't have to go to the bathroom to wash your hands. Try not to turn a light on – when light hits your baby's retina, it sends a message to the brain to wake up.

- If baby seems restless, think whether *you* need the loo or are thirsty – babies are finely attuned to their mothers, and if you are stirring, you might be disturbing her.

- Try to communicate by touch only during the night. Avoid talking and other noise.

- Try to get your partner involved. Once your baby needs fewer feeds, she might simply be waking up just for comfort. If both parents share the comforting duties, your baby will learn to be less dependent on you for *all* her security, and eventually stop needing anyone when there's no food coming.

Some co-sleeping mothers swear by breastfeeding their baby to sleep. Breast milk contains a hormone called cholecystokinin (CCK), which induces sleepiness in the baby and the mother. CCK peaks at the end of a feed, and again about half an hour to one hour after the feed – so your baby will suck, doze off, then wake up for a top-up feed which should send her into a deeper sleep. 7 Feeding can also help a baby 'tune out' stimuli such as noise and movement, and relax.

> 66 I have diligently breastfed all my children and the first two didn't sleep through the night until 14–16 months! The 3am feed has always been too good to miss! I just got used to it – it only takes me minutes to feed them and then the chemicals that are said to be released from my breast milk put us straight back to sleep.
>
> Dalvinder, mother of Amber, five, India, three, and Jasmine, 11 months 99

Night-time tips for co-sleeping:

- Breathing in unison – if a parent breathes in and out slowly and audibly, the baby will start to mimic, and relax into sleep.

- Letting your baby have contact with your body – she might face you, and rest arms or legs on your chest or stomach. The warmth and pressure is reassuring.

- Light foot massage can relax even a newborn. Later, wearing socks provides warmth and slight pressure.

- Lightly drumming fingers on the baby's back or leg, or patting rapidly but gently, helps the baby to focus and relax.

- Breathing very gently (not blowing) into the baby's face – the carbon dioxide in adults' breath relaxes a baby's breathing. But never do this if you smoke, even if it is some time since you had a cigarette.

- As a last resort, for overtired, over-stimulated babies who just can't 'let go' – try tickling! By giving a light tickle, pulling funny faces or making silly noises, you will make your baby giggle, which releases calming hormones called endorphins that will enable her to relax.

Lastly, remember that co-sleeping is not just about the baby – it is about the whole family sleeping together. If the adults go to bed irritable or stressed, it is very likely that the baby will pick up on this and won't sleep. So try to practise a good bedtime routine yourself – avoid eating large meals too late or going to bed straight after a row. You could also give yourself half a chance to feel relaxed, possibly by having a bath while your partner cuddles the baby, or by taking an evening stroll around the block.

> 66 Reducing stimuli in adult environment and behaviour at night will help babies learn the difference between night and day, though it can take some willpower not to smile and play with your baby when she's wide awake at 3am!
>
> Sara Warren, midwife 99

BY THE CLOCK

The challenges

Whereas Back to Nature techniques seem from the outside to rely heavily on instinct, By the Clock approaches at first seem to be entrenched in a confusing array of jargon, strict guru-led methods and quite a lot of conflicting advice. This is the arena where parents often feel pressured to 'pick someone' – Ford, Ferber, Hogg and many others – and stick to it religiously. If they don't follow the plan to the last letter, they think they will have failed in the Baby Sleep contest and their baby will be an uncontrollable mass of neuroses and sobs.

But if you step back from all the hype a little, actually most of these methods are simply variations on a theme.

And once you find one that suits you and your baby, things seem much simpler. Even if you fall off the wagon a bit. Or a lot.

What to do

Let's tackle the jargon first. The most common phrases you will hear are 'cry-it-out', 'Ferberisation' and 'controlled crying'.

Cry-it-out

The cry-it-out (CIO) approach can be traced to the book *The Care and Feeding of Children* by Dr Emmett Holt in 1894. Holt was a renowned American paediatrician, a 'parenting guru' of his day, and his book was a worldwide bestseller, going through 75 editions and numerous translations.

CIO is basically any sleep training method which allows a baby to cry for a specified period of time before the parent offers comfort. CIO is more of an American term, with 'controlled crying' being the corresponding term more usually used in the UK for the same kinds of methods, although these days with the internet there is much crossover. CIO methods tend also to be linked to approaches that advocate routine and structure, such as Gina Ford's *Contented Little Baby* techniques or Tracy Hogg's *Baby Whisperer*, which is also structured. But whereas Ford's is a 'It's five past seven so wake up the baby and change her nappy' kind of structure, specifying actual times throughout the day when you must move your baby from one activity to another, Hogg's is more of a 'a follows b follows c' structure, where the sequence is important but you can vary the specific timings.

Ferberisation

Ferberisation takes its name from American expert Dr Richard Ferber, and has largely come to be synonymous with CIO, although Ferber does not advocate leaving a baby to cry indefinitely.

Ferberisation usually refers to:

1. Taking steps to prepare the baby for sleep, including night-time rituals and daytime activities.

2. At bedtime, leaving the baby in bed and leaving the room.

3. Returning at progressively increasing intervals to comfort the baby – without picking her up. Extending the intervals, for instance, from three minutes, to five, to 10, until the baby is asleep.

4. Making the intervals longer on each subsequent night.

As with any approach to sleeping through the night, you will probably only try such methods from about six months. Some of the CIO experts say it can be used from four months, and a few babies are capable of sleeping through by three months – most should be able to by 18 months.

Before you try any CIO method, it is advisable to understand the concept clearly, that is you shouldn't *ignore* your baby's cries. Controlled crying doesn't not mean putting the baby in a cot, shutting the door, and going downstairs to get on with your evening.

If your baby is hungry or sick, distressed or has a soiled nappy, you should of course deal with the situation immediately. Controlled crying is simply a way of helping babies learn how to send themselves off to sleep without the use of *excessive* interventions from adults – not without *any* interventions.

> **❝** I felt that co-sleeping would be the nicest thing for Tessa, but actually the reason we gave up was that I wasn't sleeping a wink – not because Tessa was disturbing me, but because I was paranoid that every time I would drop off, or Mark would snore or roll over, that she would suffocate. I just couldn't relax. And actually, since she's been in her cot, I think she's got much better at settling herself – we don't let her cry, but it has made it easier to get a routine up and running.
>
> Jessica, mother of Tessa, 10 months **❞**

If you would like to give it a go, here is a 10-point plan example outline of a CIO approach – which you can adapt yourself, or alter to a specific expert-led method.

1. Make sure your baby is fed, clean and comfortable. Keep to a regular bedtime, with a reassuring routine which includes bathing. After changing her nappy, you could give her a cuddle.

2. Check the cot or sleeping area is safe and clear of distractions. For example are there any blankets or toys your baby might get tangled up in, and or cot bumpers and mobiles that your baby can reach?

3. Pat and comfort your baby as she lies in her cot in the darkened room, and then leave *while she is still awake*, even if she is crying. This is essential if she is to learn to settle herself.

Shut the door. If you stay in the room, your baby will sense you are there and probably cry more. Time your absence for a short period of time, up to five minutes.

4. Monitor your baby during the crying. Listen to the *type* of crying. If she is crying louder and harder once you have extended your 'intervals' to 10 minutes long, go in. It is advisable not to let a baby cry for more than this.

5. If there seems to be less urgency and less frequency between the cries, you can leave it another two minutes. She is probably near to falling asleep.

6. Be consistent every time you put your baby down. It's very hard to stand outside and listen to your baby cry, but by going in every few seconds, you will confuse her and set her up for unnecessary trauma.

7. If you do have to comfort your baby, try not to pick her up. Stroke her, or say 'shh-shh' softly.

8. Follow your instincts and do go in if you feel something is wrong. Don't ever feel you cannot check on your baby. Sometimes a baby will cry so hard that she will vomit – babies have a sensitive trigger on their gag reflex. Babies can choke on their vomit so its worth checking your baby if you have any concerns.

9. Never ignore your baby just because a method tells you to wait. If the crying is intense, do go in. Although there is no existing scientific proof that leaving your baby to cry for a *few* minutes will damage them, research has suggested that *prolonged* crying can raise a baby's blood pressure and cause other harmful effects, such as abnormally high levels of the

stress hormone Cortisol and lower growth hormone levels. This may lead to increased risk of ADHD (attention-deficit hyperactivity disorder) depression and impaired growth.

10. If in doubt – go to your baby. Trust your instincts.

Most babies will settle themselves during all sleep times within 20 minutes after about three nights. If your baby has a day where she suddenly backtracks, you can go back to comforting at shorter intervals and carry on as before.

> **6 6** We did the controlled crying thing with all three. If you stand strong together as parents, you can do it! The thing is, it really is only a few nights, and then both the baby and you are much happier.
>
> Tom, father of Rebecca, eight, Ashley, five, and Vincent, three **9 9**

Core night method

There is also a method called the 'core night method', which is a similar but gentler approach that aims to teach a baby the difference between night and day. It can be used from six weeks if the baby weighs more than 4.6kg or 10lb, has a good daytime routine and settles well in the evening, but still wakes in the night for a feed and then doesn't feed well first thing in the morning.

The core night method works on the principle that once a baby sleeps for one longer period during the night over several nights, they shouldn't be fed again during those hours slept in the 'core night'. So you have seen that your baby can last a certain length of time with no feed, you can leave her for a few minutes to settle herself back to sleep without a feed if she wakes up. If she doesn't settle, you can comfort as above, but try do this without picking her up. Babies who are putting on a good amount of weight every week can be offered a dummy (see box and expert quote for more on this) or a bottle of cool, boiled water, or if they still don't settle, the smallest possible milk feed that will see them through to morning.

The 'D' word?

Yes, quite a few of the By the Clock-style experts advocate the use of dummies to comfort babies and enable them to relax before sleep. Ford tells parents to offer a dummy but remove it as soon as the frantic sucking stops, before sleep. She believes most babies start rejecting the dummy anyway around three months, and that babies should be weaned off dummies from four months. An American study published in the British Medical Journal in 2005 found that dummies may reduce a baby's risk of cot death by 90% – although the Foundation for the Study of Infant Deaths (FSID) advises that dummies should be used consistently if at all (don't offer them some nights and not others), they should not be dipped in sweet things, and should be taken away by 12 months (see the expert quote below).

66 The advice based on this particular study [about dummies and SIDS] is that if you have given a dummy right from the start, it's best to put your baby to sleep with the dummy. The study doesn't suggest that dummies are

protective against SIDS for babies who are not in the habit of using them. It's all a bit confusing and no doubt another study at some point will further clarify this issue. However, breastfed babies shouldn't be offered a dummy at all for the first month to allow breastfeeding to become established.

Sara Warren, midwife

"

If you are going to be leaving a baby alone in a room, it is advisable that you make absolutely sure that the environment is safe. Check the room for curtain or blind cords, or electric leads, or uncovered sockets, or bulky toys or bedding. A thermometer can help you ensure the room doesn't overheat. And remember to try to make it a sleepy, cosy place to be - soft lighting with lamps or nightlights or dimmer switches, and blackout blinds, and gentle colours.

Remember that sleeping routines are for the long haul – if you chop and change too much, you will confuse your baby. And if you start setting up certain habits, be pretty sure you can live with them for a while, or you might be stuck with a routine you can't maintain.

By the Clock doesn't mean there's no room for manoeuvre, or no room for fun. This should be a calm, loving experience. If it's not after three days, try something else. Don't feel bound by the rules, see them as guidance and make them work for you and your baby. You are never going to have to take an exam in this - so the only techniques that matter are the ones that you enjoy.

> ❝ We did use controlled crying with both children. I found it incredibly hard and for the first few times I gave in and went to settle them down. When we decided that we had to break the cycle and leave them crying for a little longer each time (five minutes, next time 10 minutes, next time 15 minutes etc) it worked very quickly. Don't let anyone tell you this is easy though! I cried along with them in my own bedroom! The few days of discomfort really were only a few days though, and I wish we had been stricter with Marnie as early as we were with Freddy.

Maxine, mother of Marnie, 10, and Freddy, four ❞

FLEXI-SLEEPING

The challenges

The biggest challenge with a Flexi-Sleeper is giving them those tools they need to feel secure in a changing environment, and develop their ability to adapt.

Remember that 'chain of constants' you set up when your baby was a tiny newborn? By now that thin but strong chain that links your baby's day together and gives her security should be firmly established in her mind. In her first six months with you, your baby will have started to get used to a fluctuating set of daily circumstances, with different locations and timings for naps and bedtimes, and in the company of different people. Even small babies who might not yet need to go to a nursery or childminder might perhaps have learned to sleep at grandma's house, or with family friends, or at home but with a babysitter.

Whether you opted for a co-sleeping slant or a structured slant to your Flexi-sleeping, you will now be starting to aim for that ultimate goal: wherever and wherever they sleep, please let it be through the night!

> **"** Talise's sleeping pattern has changed a little of late — generally speaking, over the last couple of weeks (touching lots of wood when I say this) she has been sleeping for longer stretches at night. She recently went a whole seven and a half hours, which felt like such a luxury! This seems to be coinciding with her eating more solid food, as well as giving her her usual milk feeds.
>
> Dan, father of Talise, nine months **"**

What to do

If you plan to follow the Flexi-Sleeping approach, you simply need to extend that same 'chain of constants' approach to your night-time routine. Consistency is the key here – no matter how your baby's day or surroundings might differ, if you can be consistent with just a few bedtime rituals, you will encourage your baby to be adaptable and yet settled – and you will probably be the envy of all your parent friends.

By now you should already have the Flexi-Sleeping essentials – matching blankets, pyjamas or sleeping bags, a clip-on musical lullaby player or nightlight, a comforter, your photo holder, your book. And you would have spoken to your 'significant childminding others' about your preferred approach. So now all you need to do is extend this to cover all night-time awakenings, whether for food or comfort.

- Decide on a 'back to sleep drill' which you can *always* adopt *whenever* your baby wakes in the night. This has to be a drill that can be used by whichever adult is with the baby – a partner, grandparent, babysitter, childminder, nursery nurse, family friend. Therefore, by this stage, you might need to make the middle-of-the-night feeds bottle feeds – either formula or expressed milk in a bottle.

- Try to make your 'drill' short, repetitive, and use actions as well as words. So you might decide that you will pat or rub your baby's back, while 'shh-shhing' or humming.

- Offer your baby her cuddly comforter, have the photo holder within eyeshot, and play her lullaby music on a low-volume setting.

- If baby needs feeding, you can offer the bottle in the dark or in a subdued light, and not talk during the feed. This is because baby needs not to associate these feeds with your voice alone – she needs to be able to accept this bottle from whichever carer is with her.

- Create some special 'sleepy words' that you will use *after* the feed, when the baby is drowsy. These are cue words, to be said in a gentle voice every time your baby is drifting off to sleep having been disturbed: 'Close your eyes, everything's fine, sleepy time now'. Eventually your baby will develop sleep associations with these words, and you can use them to resettle them if they stir in the night. Teach your 'significant childminding others' and your partner the words, and ask them to use them likewise.

- It doesn't matter if you are using this routine while co-sleeping or with a baby sleeping in their own room – wherever the baby is, keep the same drill. Let the familiar objects and the familiar drill be the comfort, not the person giving it.

Will Flexi-Sleeping stop us bonding?

Don't worry that this method will compromise your ability to bond with your baby – a secure baby feels loved, and you can spend extra 'bonding times' with your baby during non-sleeping hours – create a special 'storytime with Mummy' slot on a certain afternoon when you might return early from work, for instance, where you curl up on some cushions and spend time together. Or a 'Saturday Special lie-in' time when she first wakes up and can snuggle with you in your bed or in the sofa while your partner makes breakfast.

If you know that your baby will shortly have to adapt to a major upheaval in her routine – such as starting a day nursery, or going to a childminder, or spending some days with a relative or a separated partner – then it is a good idea to start to introduce more variation in her *home* routine in advance of the change, so that she is prepared to be flexible. So, if your set-up allows it, perhaps sleep in a different bed some nights with your baby – a bed in the guest room, for example, or a mattress on the living room floor. Or move your baby from the cot in her nursery to a crib in your room for a night, or perhaps in with older siblings (making sure the room is first baby-proofed and that siblings are supervised). Or go to stay with grandma for a few 'practice runs'.

Even if the change will not affect night-times, such as nursery or a childminder, it will still alter the daily rhythms of the baby, and probably exhaust her initially, so a little forethought will help her prepare and adapt.

One more thing you can do is leave a small object (soft and baby-proof) with your child whenever you have to be away from her – for work, or for an access visit for instance – and then remember to 'collect' it back from her when you are reunited. It could be a tiny teddy, or a stuffed object. You can start doing this even when she is too small to understand, because later she will feel reassured by the ritual – by playing up the giving and getting back of the object, you are acknowledging your desire to be with her – and she also has a 'displacement' object she can focus on positively when she misses you.

Lastly, and possibly in tandem with your special object, you can reinforce a 'mantra' of reassurance that again, you could have started using with your baby as soon as she was born, but which she will come to fully understand and take comfort from when she is much older. This should be something that you say at bedtime whenever you are with your baby, and also when you have to leave your baby with another person, and when you return to her. It could be something like: 'Remember Mummy loves you, wherever we both are' or 'Here's a kiss from Mummy, to tuck behind your ear and remind you I love you always'.

" Kate and I did the 'shh–shhing' thing at bedtimes, and we also had a little 'mantra' we'd use which was just 'Mason go night-nights' repeated over and over. When he was about 18 months he'd even say it himself without being prompted when he was tired.

Jon, father of Mason, three

"

MULTIPLE MADNESS

The challenges

Ever run a relay race in a straitjacket while balancing an egg on your head, having had no sleep for seven nights on the trot and no proper food for two days? Probably not. But from what I can gather from parents of multiples, getting their babies to sleep through the night would make that relay race seem like a walk in the park. However you look at it, getting two or more babies to sleep through the night has got to be harder than getting one to sleep through. For starters, there's the simple logistical issues such as one baby waking the other up, and one parent only having one pair of hands (and just one set of breasts, if you are breastfeeding). And then you have to add to that the possibility that your babies are premature (as twins often are), and may have been born with a low birth weight. This means they may well meet developmental milestones later than average – their age from birth is actually misleading, because of the prematurity. Doctors often refer to twins' 'adjusted age', which means calculating their age from their due date rather than their delivery date to give parents an idea of where they would normally be.

The other complicating factor is that one baby will often lag a few weeks behind the other – which is a joy when you have one baby who is able to sleep for six hours straight, but the other can only do four, and your schedule is so all-consuming because they are out of kilter that you get no sleep yourself.

How well your babies sleep will often depend more on their weight than their age.

If one baby is larger than the other, she will probably sleep through the night first. Identical twins tend to sleep through at almost identical ages, though, whereas fraternal twins' sleep patterns may be more independent, especially if they are very different in size or temperament. If it is any consolation, this probably suggests that an ability to sleep through is somehow genetically pre-determined – so at least you can tell yourself that the reason they are still awake at three in the morning isn't because you are doing it all wrong.

> ❝ The twins were about four months when they slept through the night. By this time they were in their own rooms. We did use the controlled crying method and were quite firm.
>
> I don't think the breast/bottle made a difference as I breastfed our elder daughter Lily and she slept through from about three months. I do think solids can make a difference – James really began to settle in general when he went onto solids.
>
> Callie, mother of Lily, four, and James and Sophia, two ❞

What to do

Strategies for getting twins or multiples to sleep through the night really echo those for single babies – but with more of a focus on the structured, timetabled approach. A good bedtime routine is helpful – bath, stories, cuddles, dim lighting. Some experts believe that twins up to six months old sleep better together, or in a family bed – and if you are breastfeeding, there is a lot to be said for learning to do it lying down, and being able to doze while baby suckles.

As previously mentioned, the golden rule is also that if one baby wakes for a feed, always wake the other too, to synchronise their schedules.

Until they are sleeping for longer stretches, you can also try a 'team' approach (see box). This technique allows both parents to get at least five hours of sleep a night, so that neither feels completely exhausted and overwhelmed by lack of sleep.

> **❝** Our twins had such different sleep patterns – complete opposite in fact. When Hannah was fast asleep, Robert was awake and ready to be fed. At first, I felt awful waking Hannah up from her deep sleep, but within a week, I got over this and slowly established a routine for them both, and was just about manageable for me!
>
> Trisha, mother of Hannah and Robert, three **❞**

The team approach

You need to agree a schedule so that one of you is on duty while the other sleeps. For instance, mum could be on duty from 9pm until 2am, while dad sleeps, and then dad takes over from 2am until the morning. Or mum sleeps from early evening when dad gets home from work, and then she wakes up to allow dad to go to bed by midnight.

Once the babies are able to go for longer stretches, you might want to consider putting them in separate cots. You could choose to put these two cots in the same room where the babies can still see each other – many parents and experts seem to think this is the best option because they can still derive comfort from each other, and they don't seem to be disturbed too much by each other's crying. Others advocate separate rooms entirely, perhaps for older babies, so that they get used to a calm, sleep-inducing environment with no disturbance at all.

Other techniques for encouraging longer sleep periods at night for twins include:

- 'Cluster' feeding in the early evening. This means giving two milk feeds within a relatively short period of time – say before and then after a bath. The feeling is that this will 'stock up' the babies' stomachs and enable them to sleep without waking due to hunger. Gina Ford advocates this in her routines for twins. Feeding tiny babies after bathing is recommended because they are less likely to bring up part of the feed.

- In days gone by, one method used to be adding a spoonful of cereal to milk feeds before bedtime. The purpose was as above, to fill the stomach and delay hunger. However, this is now very controversial and isn't recommended. The practice of introducing solids to small babies in this way increases the chances of infection and allergies, particularly regarding gluten-based cereals. The Department of Health in conjunction with the World Health Organisation recommends exclusive breastfeeding whenever possible for the first six months of life. For formula-fed babies, weaning advice is the same, with no solid foods until after the first six months of life and definitely not before four months.

- Letting go of the last feed. Many parents feel that once babies are only waking for one night-time feed, and have managed the odd night without waking at all, they are ready to be 'encouraged' to let go of that last feed by having the milk watered down a little. This can be done with breast milk or formula (add a little sterile water (once-boiled water from the kettle) to expressed breast milk, and simply add fewer scoops of formula to the same amount of water for bottles). The idea is to water down gradually, until eventually you are only offering straight water on the odd occasions that they still wake up. This will gradually wean them from their night-time feed. A good rule of thumb that your babies are ready to do this is when they still wake for a night-time feed, but aren't very interested in their first morning feed – at this stage, they are better off missing the night one and having the appetite to polish off their morning one with gusto.

- Most parents of twins have many times when they feel quite despairing that their babies will ever learn to coordinate themselves and sleep through the night. Sleep deprivation isn't used as an instrument of torture for nothing – these early months will be the most challenging of your life. But with a little structure, a good calm approach and a hands-on team effort from family, it will pass. There is a lot of support and advice available from organisations such as the Twins & Multiple Births Association (Tamba; www.tamba.org.uk). And believe that you will one day wake up and realise that both (or all!) of your babies have slept through, and it is seven in the morning. Take heart – at least you will be getting two (or more) bouts of sleep disturbance over, in one simultaneous go.

> " Luke and Perry slept through at about three months, which is early for twins – but I'm sure that's because they shared a cot and comforted each other. When one or the other was poorly. I'd sometimes take him in with me, and then the other one wouldn't sleep well at all. "

Jenny, mother of Luke and Perry, seven

SLEEPING THROUGH THE NIGHT

Remember that children don't actually 'sleep through the night' properly, without any disturbance or waking, until they are probably three or four years old. What most parents mean by sleeping through is that their children are sleeping without disturbing them – i.e. when they do wake, they can settle themselves quickly and quietly without becoming upset or needing comfort. So don't get too hung up on the whole concept – yes, this is desirable, but it's not a concrete thing. Babies are humans – just like adults, they can have good nights and bad nights. Things change, things pass. Keep to your chosen approach, stay calm, and you will get the sleep that you, and your baby, need.

❝ Remembering that babies are small people with individual personalities and preferences can take a lot of the tension out of trying to establish sleep patterns. The more calm and adaptable parents can be, the more relaxed and secure the baby will feel, whichever methods are adopted. **❞**

Sara Warren, midwife

3

Making the Move

66 The amount of sleep required by the average person is five minutes more. 99

Wilson Mizener

J ust as you think you have reached some semblance of order, and the concept of 'a good night's sleep' seems almost achievable again, you face the next challenge: making the move.

This can mean different things to different families. For Back to Nature families, this might mean baby making a move from the family bed, or bedroom, into a cot or a room of their own. For By the Clock families, it might come at a later age, and mean a move from cot to toddler or big bed. For Multiple Madness families, it might mean twins or multiples moving from family bed to cot, or from shared cot to separate cots, or from shared rooms to separate rooms. And for Flexi-Sleepers, it could mean any combination of the above.

What is the same for all families, though, is that you face a period of transition, which is going to be demanding for you and unsettling for your baby. She might be feeling insecure about having to go to sleep alone or further away from parents or siblings. You might be feeling nervous about your baby not being so much under your watchful eye – worried about safety, and unable to settle to sleep yourself. And on top of all that, if your baby is making the move into a bed, or has worked out how to climb out of a cot, you have to deal with gleeful escapees and mini-explorers who have figured out that 'up time' isn't restricted to Mum and Dad's idea of a reasonable morning start any more.

Don't worry – by now you will have started to realise that with babies nothing lasts very long. However frustrating or challenging your baby's current phase is, it will pass, and within months you will hardly remember it.

Whichever *Baby Sleep Bible* approach you are following, just stick to your guns and take the appropriate measures to make the Big Move as stress-free as possible for you and your baby.

BACK TO NATURE

When to do it?

There is no right time to move your baby from your bed, or your bedroom, into her own cot, bed or room. When it happens will depend on two things: your feelings on how it is working for you, your baby and the whole family; and your baby's own preferences. Some parents report that children will happily bed share until they are six, seven or older, whereas others say that by the age of three or four, or sometimes a lot younger, children suddenly decide they need their own space and request a separate bed or room to themselves.

Even some very young babies decide that a cuddle at bedtime is enough, but they want to sleep alone. Sensitive babies, who might react irritably to loud or sudden noises, or have allergies, or react to rough textures against their skin, for instance, will often be babies who sleep much better in their own space. And sometimes the reason will be an external one, such as having another baby on the way, or simply a desire for more night-time privacy.

Whenever it happens, though, there are things you can do to make that transition easier (see next section).

Generally speaking, the younger the baby, the easier the change will be.

Depending on your baby's age and personality, the move might take anywhere from a few days to several months. Try not to worry if she doesn't accept this new set of circumstances overnight – if you are relaxed about it, she will pick up your cues and be less likely to dig her heels in.

> We were desperate to have a 'family bed' before our eldest Kitty was born. We were all set up for it. But it turned out that Kitty just couldn't go to sleep if she was being held, or was too close to us. She needed space to go to sleep. So she ended up in a wooden crib next to us from that first couple of weeks, so we at least felt close to her. She then moved into her own cot in her nursery when she was about five months. Even now (she's two) she still only cosies up for cuddles on her terms, and doesn't like being held when she's tired. With Finn, we just went straight to the crib option.
>
> Mary-anne, mother of Kitty, two, and Finn, four months

How to do it

- You may find it easier to think small steps, rather than one fell swoop. Maybe make the move with just some of your baby's sleep times, not all – for instance, start with nap times in the day. Remember that babies shouldn't be left alone in a full-height adult bed once they start to roll anyway, so now is a good time for this.

- If your baby is very young, she might find it easier to move from your bed to a Moses basket or carry cot and then into a full-sized cot. Or move baby from sleeping between you and your partner to a 'sidecar' arrangement, and then gradually over a few days or weeks raise the fourth side of the cot, and then move the cot away from the bed, and eventually into another room.

- Another gradual arrangement is to move baby into her own room, but sleep in there with her on a mattress for a while. Having you nearby will ease the change. A less drastic form of this is just sitting in a chair in the room while she falls asleep. If she keeps sitting or standing up, gently lay her on her back and return to your chair. Eventually she will understand that you are not going to pick her up, and that it is time to sleep. You might want to use this time to read a book (yes, a book! Remember those?)

- Or you could place your baby in a cot or crib for the first part of the night and if she wakes for a feed or for comfort later on, bring her back into your bed at this stage. Gradually make this later and later in the night until she is going through in the cot.

- If you are still breastfeeding or bottle feeding at night, start to introduce feeds in a rocking chair in your room or hers, instead of doing it in bed.

- If you child is older, you could give her a sleeping bag (perhaps on a little futon mattress, or one of those blow-up children's sleepers) next to your bed in your bedroom, and then move it across the room, and then into her own room.

❝ I wanted to co-sleep, and my husband was willing to give it a go, but eventually after about seven months we both had to admit that having Lois in with us had completely blitzed our sex life. To have sex, we had to plan it — and that made it feel like yet another chore to tick off. Now Lois has made the move to her own room, and we're all very happy!

Becky, mother of Lois, 13 months **❞**

It is only natural for a baby or child to feel some trepidation at losing their prime spot next to their parent(s). A toddler or older child will express this by coming back into your room in the middle of the night for comfort. It's best to remain calm and positive, and just lead your child back to her own space and sit with her for a while. Or you could keep that little mattress by your bedside just for 'emergency visits' – it can be phased out once she is more sure of herself.

Some things you can do to make sure the Big Move doesn't prove more traumatic than it needs to are listed below.

- Try not to overload. So if your child is sick, teething, approaching a big milestone such as crawling or walking, or adjusting to a new home, caregiver, schedule or sibling, you might want to postpone the big move. It may be better not to mess with her routine until the dust settles.

- Consider letting your baby share a room with an older sibling if she has one. Big brothers and sisters offer their own brand of comfort.

- Celebrate the move to another room with her – let her pick out some new duvet covers, or wall charts, or a lamp, or some fairy lights.

- Try to make the new space your baby will occupy as restful and reassuring as it can be – blackout blinds, soft lighting, maybe a lullaby CD, or some 'white noise', such as a small fan or air purifier. And check the sleeping surface too – if your baby is startled as soon as she touches the crib mattress, try putting a warm blanket under her before you lay her down, and make her mattress smell the same as your bed by sleeping with her sheet for a night before putting it on.

Lastly, give lots and lots of comfort.

This will have two benefits:

- It will help comfort your baby through a difficult time. Remember that a newborn doesn't even realise that Mum is a separate person until at least three months old, and until nine months she won't understand the concept of 'object permanence' – that something, including you, still exists even when she can no longer see it. Even older children need to know you are coming back – their perception of the passing of time is different to ours, so even if we say we'll check on them in 20 minutes, they might feel that that is like hours.

- It will also help you with your feelings about making the move. Even if you and your partner are fully ready for your baby to move from your bed – indeed, looking forward to it – there may still be a part of you that feels a mixture of regret, or nostalgia, or even guilt. Making time for lots of cuddles and quiet time and bonding, in your room or in theirs, will ensure that the bonds you have worked so hard to create will continue to be strong.

Eventually you will be able to leave your baby in her cot or room, kiss her goodnight, and walk away with no crying. Your baby will have learned that her new sleeping place is safe, that sleep is not a lonely or scary experience, and that you will come if she needs you. And you can go to sleep in your own bed knowing that everyone is safe and happy.

BY THE CLOCK

When to do it?

This is the bit when, as By the Clock parents, you might be forgiven for feeling just the tiniest bit smug. For if you have chosen a structured, routine-based approach, the chances are that your baby is already in her own cot, and will very likely be in her own room too. If she has been in a cot or Moses basket but hasn't yet made the transition to her own room, then following the Back to Nature advice above will be helpful to you. But once your baby is in her own nursery or bedroom, the Big Move for you will involve the transition from cot to 'big bed'.

Again, there is no set time when a child should be moved from a cot to a bed. Most will make the change anywhere between 18 months and three-and-a-half years. Reasons which might prompt you or your child to make the move include:

- Outgrowing the cot, or learning to climb out of it – it is safer for children to be climbing out of bed than out of a cot when they could injure themselves and have further to fall.

- Having another baby on the way who will need to take possession of the cot. If this is the case, have your child make the move at least six to eight weeks before the new baby arrives, to prevent feelings of jealousy and sibling rivalry when she sees the new arrival take her place. Or wait until the newborn is three or four months old (put him in a Moses basket or crib to start with) and then make the move when feelings have settled a little.

- You plan to potty train your child, and so she will need to be able to get up herself in the night to go to the toilet.

However, try to time the Big Move so that it doesn't coincide with other life-changing transitions such as potty training (see above) or starting nursery. First-born children especially can get very attached to their cot so it is important not to underestimate the upheaval that giving it up may cause.

How to do it

Things you can do to ease the way are:

- Put the bed in the same place as the cot used to be, so that the child's perspective when lying down has not changed.

- Or keep the cot *and* the bed in the room for a while, so that the reassurance of the cot is still there. Let the child choose which one they will sleep in – we did this with Evie, and although she was a bit wobbly at the thought of losing her cot, as soon as she had that choice, she chose the bed from day one, and let us get rid of the cot within three days.

- Let your child sleep with their old cot blanket, even if it's too small, or in their familiar baby sleeping bag.

- If it's going to be a new bed, let your child go with you to help pick it out, and let her help choose the sheets and duvet covers.

- Buy a pretty new lamp or nightlight, and maybe decorate the ceiling with luminous stars and moons.

- Leave the door open a little or play comforting lullaby music in your child's room to make bedtime comforting.

- Consider instigating a slightly different 'big bed routine' which will help her settle into her new surroundings – have a quiet time before bed, pack away toys and prepare the bedroom as a quiet place to rest, rather than an exciting play room. Dim the lights, pull the curtains, line up the teddies into their night-time positions – anything to draw a close to the day and prepare for sleep.

- Avoid getting stressed if she keeps getting out of bed. If she comes out of the room, try to firmly take her back and tuck her in and avoid interacting with her too much, so that she realises that getting up isn't actually that much fun. If she simply gets out of bed to play, and then falls asleep on the floor, let her and then just put her back into bed. At least you will still have had your adult evening time, and you won't have made bedtime antagonistic.

> **"** We went for a toddler bed because a big single bed just seemed too enormous for Sara. We moved her a while before Phoebe came along so she didn't associate the move with the new baby, and we threw her a little 'big bed' bedtime party with Granny and her teddies.
>
> Gemma, mother of Sara, two, and Phoebe, two months

Safety check

Once your baby is out of a cot and 'free range', you will need to be aware of safety issues that haven't yet arisen. It is wise to do a complete safety check at this point, just to reassure yourself that everything is ready to go. Things you need to think about are:

- A guard rail, especially if it's a full-sized single bed rather than a low toddler bed, or doesn't have its own built-in side rails. You can now buy inflatable 'bed bolsters' which take 20 seconds to inflate and pack away into a small, light bag – good for holidays, and softer than the metal ones for at home. You could also put a thick rug or pillows next to the bed for a soft landing.

- Window locks – toddlers love to climb. You can buy locks which allow a small gap – useful in summer – but check that this gap is smaller than your child's head.

- Curtain and blind cords – they love to play with these, but they could strangle your child. Tie them up high in a secure knot, or cut them, or you can get a small plastic gadget that keeps them safe.

- Electrical appliances – lamp bulbs can get very hot. Put them up high if you have one, and explain to children not to drape fabric over them (this had to be stressed with Evie, who is such a girlie girl that she likes to 'prettify' everything by decorating it with things. Even our ironing board has some glittery red ribbon round one of the legs.) Consider nightlights instead. Also check flexes and leads – you can get gadgets to contain these, too. And cover all unused sockets with a socket cover.

- Stairways – fit gates so they don't wander out of their room sleepily in the night, become disorientated and fall.

- Toilets – consider a safety lock on the lid to prevent small toddlers from falling in.

- Pillows – these are still dangerous for children under two, as are bulky duvets. They are a suffocation risk. You can use baby sleeping bags on a flat mattress instead.

Once you have got everything set, approach the move with firm but gentle guidance. Try talking about the new bed in a positive light, and maybe refer to the 'big girl's rooms' or the 'big boy's rooms'. If, once they have made the move, things seem to be falling apart a little and your child seems stressed, some extra things to help it all along are given below.

- Try to make your child's new space as appealing as possible. Accessories which give off light are a good way to get rid of the night-time frights. You can buy child-safe fairy lights which are cool to touch, and lights which project rainbows or moons on the wall or ceiling. Even a child's torch might be a reassuring bedside accessory for an older toddler.

- Make sure your child is wearing warm bedtime clothes to allow for the covers falling off. Maybe add bed socks during winter.

- Try a little lavender oil on a hanky near the pillow for children who can't 'let go'. Or you can buy lavender-stuffed cuddly toys which can be microwaved to make them warm and fragrant.

- If your child keeps getting up time and again at bedtime, try a 'treat bank'. Fill a jar or container with a number of similar objects - big pebbles, for instance (big enough not to be swallowed!) or coloured pom-poms, or tickets which your child can design and colour in herself. Start every week on a

Sunday night with a set number of these in the container. For every time she gets up during the week (excluding getting up for toilet visits or illness), take one item out. For every night she goes straight to bed and sleeps, add one in. At the end of the week, count them up and decide on a 'value' for each item, for instance 10 pence, or 10 minutes of story time with Dad, then add up and give her her treat.

- If your child thinks 5am is a good time for breakfast, try one of those light timers designed to turn your lamps on to prevent burglaries. Set it to your chosen morning wake-up time, and set a rule that she doesn't get out of bed before the light goes on. If she wakes up before then, she can play quietly in bed. A variation on this is a radio alarm clock set for a certain time – she can't get up before the music starts playing.

> ❝ Our lot were all allowed to choose something to stick or paint on their walls when they moved from their cots into beds. Rebecca chose some flower transfers, Ashley had a fairy frieze thing, and Vincent had luminous stars on the ceiling. It worked a treat.
>
> Tom, father of Rebecca, eight, Ashley, five, and Vincent, three ❞

Finally, remember that moving into a bed is an exciting step towards your child becoming more independent. Make a fuss – let them know how proud of her you are. And if you are feeling a little sad that your baby is growing up a little, remember that beds can have a great benefit for parents too – finally, there is somewhere soft and comfy to sit for all those cosy bedtime stories and cuddles. This is a time to reinforce the bond between you

– you have worked hard to nurture your baby into a confident little person, and eventually her bed and her bedroom will be a special place for her, somewhere she associates with reassurance, comfort and happy times alone and with you.

FLEXI-SLEEPING

When to do it?

If you are Flexi-Sleeping with your baby, you will probably be interested in the advice given either in the Back to Nature section or in the By the Clock sections of this chapter. The chances are your baby will already be relatively flexible about where she sleeps, having already got used to a varying sleep pattern and location. But making the move can still be traumatic for her – so don't make the mistake of simply assuming that your adaptable little one won't need the same softly-softly approach as any other baby.

How to do it

There are some additional things you can add to these in order to continue to help your baby be flexible and adaptable once she makes the move from your bed to a cot, or from a cot to a bed or room of her own.

This is the time to introduce a few new rituals and items into your 'chain of constants', that backbone that helps your child feel settled and secure no matter where she is sleeping.

These constants need to be aids to getting your child to accept a new sleeping space, or a set of new sleeping spaces. If the move is from co-sleeping to a cot in your room, you could add another little 'mantra' to your 'sleepy words' that you say each time you lay your baby down in it. 'Into the cosy cot we go', or 'Cot time for sleepy babies' or something that suits you – but which you stick to, and which you and any other caregiver repeat without fail *every* time your baby goes into a cot of any kind. By reinforcing this comforting but purposeful phrase, saying it in a soft, sing-song way, you will teach your baby to expect and be reassured by the words which will act as a trigger to remind her of cosy home bedtimes, even when she is away from home.

> 66 We went for the big single bed option, because that's what my mother already had at her house, and we wanted to keep things as similar as possible. But we bought a bed rail so he felt a bit more secure, and lined his teddies up along it.
>
> Jon, father of Mason, three 99

If the move is into a bed or room of their own, then you have even more scope to lengthen your 'chain'. In this situation, the mantra could instead be something along the lines of 'into Big Boy's cosy bed' or 'into the princess grotto we go', as you enter the room to prepare for bedtime. And after this you could:

● Have a specific 'Bed Ted' who sits on the pillow in the day, but becomes part of the bedtime routine at night. This might be a teddy with a zip compartment to store pyjamas in, or maybe one of those teddies which glow or sing a lullaby when you press their tummy. Bed Ted should be brought into the routine – 'Bed Ted says have you cleaned your teeth?' 'Bed Ted says time to put on your nightie'. And when it's time to lie down and go to sleep, Bed Ted should have a place where he sits through the night – at the foot of the bed, or on the floor next to the bed head. When your child has to sleep at another house, Bed Ted should go too, and other caregivers should be aware of the ritual.

- Make that bedtime music that you have played since birth – from your nightlight or music player – a little more grown-up now. Maybe treat your child to a new, 'big room' CD player and buy a special bedtime CD. But choose one specific kind of music to play, so that it becomes a 'constant' that can be duplicated in other houses.

- Now that your baby is slightly older, make a special 'sign' for her that you always give just as you leave the room, and that will let her know that she will be safe and protected through the night. This could be a religious thing if you want – any religion. It could be a short prayer, or something else – for instance, I never put either Evie or Charlie to bed anywhere without making a small sign of the cross on their foreheads and saying 'God Bless'. When Evie was going through her 'night-time monsters' phase, and would ask how I could keep the ghosties from coming in through her walls if I was downstairs watching TV, I would simply say to her that nothing bad could happen because she had had her 'God Bless'. And she accepted this, because I consistently said it with conviction. It doesn't have to be a Christian or a religious thing though – you might give a kiss in a certain way, or leave a small crystal where she can see it on a shelf or bedside table, or have a 'family saying' which you say together, such as 'Sleep safe 'til morning and know that we love you' – or even the traditional 'Sleep tight, don't let the bed bugs bite!' All those old sayings were said for the same purpose – ritual and reassurance. Again, share this information with any other carers at whose houses your child needs to sleep.

- If your child feels restless or nervous at night, think of one more 'constant' which will reassure them that, if she tries hard to settle but have an 'emergency' need for you, you will come and you won't be angry. You might find that it is overused in the first few nights, but once she feels secure you will usually find she uses it rarely. This could be a small hand bell to ring, if it won't disturb other siblings; or just a phrase that is only used for this purpose, such as 'Crisis Cuddle!', to be whispered down the stairs. Tell other carers to be aware of this.

> ❝ We moved Fionn to the big bed when he was about 18 months because he was climbing out and we worried that he might hurt himself. When he first went in the bed he couldn't sleep and said there were monsters at the end etc.... what I did was lay his toys around him at about the old parameters of the cot so that the bed didn't feel so vast and he had some friendly faces to look at. After nights of struggling to get him to sleep, he stayed in bed all night the first night I tried this.
>
> Lisa, mother of Fionn, three, and Bridget, 10 months ❞

As always, if you are Flexi-Sleeping, it's all about repetition and consistency, even though it's for families that like or need flexibility and change. However, the more you keep these small, achievable 'constants' in your child's life – and most of these take little or no daily effort – the more you will be rewarded with a child who can cope with the family's need to go with the flow, or with the odd unexpected change of location or timing, or different face.

The repetitive rituals and familiar objects are the tether that will allow your little one to be able to fly with confidence – but still know that there is a safety rope there and that someone is going to pull her safely back down to earth.

MULTIPLE MADNESS

When to do it?

Making the move with twins, triplets or more might seem like something of a blackly humorous concept – after all, aren't you 'on the move' all the time? In fact, the Big Move with multiples is more likely to be a series of moves. You may well already have moved your babies from a shared family bed into Moses baskets, or a shared cot – or indeed started off that way from the beginning.

But what happens when you make that final move into their own room in cots or 'big beds' – and how will you know if they're ready for it?

Firstly, it will depend on the temperament of your babies – whether from birth they have sought and are used to the comfort of each other, or whether they seem to rub each other up the wrong way when in close proximity – and on whether your twins or multiples are same sex, or fraternal and of different genders.

You may find it easier to have same-sex twins share a bedroom – from a purely practical point of view of decor and toy space – than different gender multiples. Some multiples with older siblings might join separate bedrooms with an older brother or sister – a boy twin with an older brother, a girl twin with an older sister.

There is also the question of developmental readiness, and synchronisation: identical twins are more likely to settle into nap times and need a similar amount of night-time sleep at a similar age, whereas fraternal twins develop as differently as any other siblings, and may clash by having different sleep patterns and disturbing each other.

Although multiples tend to remain in their cots for longer than single babies – many parents of multiples wait until their children are two or even three years old, providing the cots are big enough – you might be propelled into the move to separate beds or rooms if they start to disturb each other or you. Some parents report a kind or 'cooing relay' that twins keep up between themselves while in your room – little babblings and noises to reassure each other but which leave you unable to sleep. Others say that when co-sleeping twins (whether with each other or in a family bed) reach the age around six months when they are able to roll about and move more, they start to squabble or elbow each other accidentally with flailing limbs, and keep each other awake.

Advantages to sharing a room are that some multiples go to sleep better and feel calmer in the presence of each other, and will play happily together in the early morning before you need to go in. Disadvantages are that you will have to pack a lot of clothing and toys into that shared space, and the babies might well egg each other on when misbehaving, and keep each other awake. Nap time becomes playtime if there's a playmate in the same room! Also, it is easier to encourage older multiples to clean up and take care of their stuff if they have a separate space – shared rooms often mean squabbling over possessions, and blaming mess on each other.

Advantages of separate rooms are that the children might sleep more soundly and settle in a more restful atmosphere, and feel more secure that their own special toys and possessions are private and belong to them; disadvantages are that separated multiples may feel compelled to get up more often in an attempt to be with each other, and that some multiples seem not to be able to fall asleep without the reassuring proximity of their sibling.

It may take some experimentation and a good deal of patience to figure out your best combination – and it may also come down to prosaic matters such as the limitations of a home's space and number of available bedrooms.

How to do it

So what can you do to ease the transition for babies who will share a room with each other?

- You may want to buy toddler beds due to their popularity as a transition between cots and big beds, and due to their compact nature which means you can fit more into one room. They are expensive though, especially in duplicate – another option is to use normal single beds, but take the mattresses and box springs off the frame and place directly on the ground for safety. They can be reassembled into regular beds when your multiples are ready for them.

- If your babies have been used to sharing a cot, push the two mattresses together to form an oversized bed, so that they can begin the transition by being close to each other just as they have in the past (make sure there is no gap between the two mattresses that they can get stuck in). As the children grow, you could then choose to split the beds up again and move them slowly away from each other to opposite sides of the room or to different rooms so that they aren't tossing and turning on top of each other all night.

- If you find that your twins or multiples play mischief with each other during nap times and at night – parents report such exuberant mischief that entire rooms are trashed, and drawers upturned in glee – you might try putting them in baby sleeping bags (they go up to big sizes) and taking everything out of the room other than bedding for a short while, so that there is less to be thrown about or played with, and they therefore lose interest and go to sleep more quickly.

> " We put Luke and Perry into their own room in two different cots pushed close together. They seemed to feel reassured that they could still hear each other's snuffles and breathing. As they got older, we moved the cots apart a bit. And when they eventually went into beds, they had one end of the room each, with different colours on the walls and different bedding and furniture. "
>
> Jenny, mother of Luke and Perry, seven

And what can you do for babies who will go into their own separate rooms?

- If your babies are to go into separate rooms, you might want to do this at an earlier age rather than leaving it. Smaller babies will adapt to change quite quickly, but toddlers can be very sensitive to separation and it may feel to them like a punishment rather than a privilege. At toddler age, they may also be going through other big changes such as potty training and starting pre-school, which will add to their feelings of confusion and disruption.

- If you are leaving it until later, think about doing it before your children begin their first year at school: this is a time when multiples might appreciate a private place to do homework, or simply to 'come down' after a hectic full day at school. For twins and multiples, this is also often one of the first times that they may have to learn to stand on their own feet and develop their individual identities, perhaps going into separate classes for the first time, and making separate friends. For this reason, making the move *during* that first year might again prove too much disruption during a difficult time.

To ease the separation pangs that your babies might feel sleeping away from each other, provide a comforter, blankie or teddy to cuddle – perhaps a special new one that sings or glows. You could even dress it in a sleepsuit that the other baby has slept in, so those comforting smells are there.

66 When we first separated Hannah and Robert, we had a problem as they had both got attached to the same blanket at night. After a few nights of crying, we eventually solved the problem by cutting it in half!

Trisha, mother of Hannah and Robert, three 99

- The other thing the babies might miss is noise – all those little sniffles, babbles and movements that they have become used to. Consider some 'white noise' from a fan or purifier, or you can even buy special CDs of white noise to play to babies. If you have the patience, try recording the babies for a few hours on a night *before* they make the move, and then duplicating the recording onto CD or tape to play back to them in their separate rooms – then they will have the familiar sounds of each other ready at the push of a button.

> **“** We put the babies into cots in their own rooms at about three months. We were exhausted and they just kept waking each other up when they both slept in our room. We didn't ease them into their cots – we just did it! For me, sleep (or lack of it) is just the hardest thing. Andrew and I started the twins' sleep routine as soon as we all felt settled and really are quite rigid. With the controlled crying we stuck to it – often through tears and we often felt cruel – but it really has paid dividends. The twins are excellent sleepers, they delight in their routine and I firmly believe it helps to make them secure, confident and happy.
>
> Callie, mother of Lily, four, and James and Sophia, two **”**

Whichever option you choose, remember to take the usual steps of establishing a good, calm bedtime routine, and setting up the room or rooms to be dimly lit, cosy, appealing places to rest and sleep. With patience, and with the courage to recognise the individual needs, developmental stages and personalities of your babies, you will find the right way for your family – and if you stick to it with gentle determination, your Multiple Madness will evolve into separate serenity!

66 The Department of Health recommends that babies share a room with their mothers for the first six months of life and this should be taken into consideration when thinking about alternative sleeping arrangements.

Sara Warren, midwife   99

4

Nap Times and Daytime Sleeping

66 No day is so bad it can't be fixed with a nap. 99

Carrie Snow

If you are a prospective parent, the word 'sleep' invariably brings to mind sepia-tinted images of peaceful babies with chubby flushed cheeks snoozing peacefully in their crib or next to you as you gaze upon them adoringly. A very short time after your baby arrives, you are forced to try to reconcile this fantasy with the reality of night-time wailing, cheeks flushed with frustration and endless walks up and down the landing singing 'Old MacDonald' but finding that you have run out of animals.

After following the previous chapters' advice, you hopefully reach – eventually – a kind of semi-peaceful compromise, where your chosen approach has led to a reasonable amount of good nights' sleeps, and you and your baby have found a night-time routine which works for you. But it doesn't end there, because while you might have your evenings and night-times sorted, what about during the day? Enter the chaotic world of the nap. Such a short little word – but it can cause a lot of upheaval.

The problem with naps is threefold:

1. There are a lot more variations on nap times than there are on night-time sleeping, so there is more confusion and less definite advice to follow.

2. Most adults have a lot more juggling of other commitments to do by day than by night.

3. It quickly becomes obvious that whatever you do about your baby's sleep in the day will have a direct effect on how well, and for how long, she settles at night.

No pressure there, then.

So how can you take the stress out of daytime naps?

As with night-time sleeping, every baby will have a different temperament, natural body rhythm and rate of development. This means they will have different nap requirements, and will prefer different means of taking a nap. Some babies nap for long stretches from the start and like napping in their cot or your bed, and others are 'cat-nappers' who take shorter naps in buggies or cars. So if your baby doesn't nap like those of your friends, don't worry. This doesn't mean you are doing it wrong.

When do babies nap?

Sleep is, undeniably, vital for babies and young children because their brains and bodies are developing at an extraordinary rate. And night-time rest isn't enough – they need to top up with regular naps.

- As a newborn, your baby will probably sleep for two to four hours at a time, throughout the day and night. At this stage, there's no difference between night-time sleep and naps, so don't try to create one – just let your baby sleep for as long as she needs to.

- By six to eight weeks old, your baby will sleep less often but for longer periods of time, and will start to need two to four naps a day, or more.

- By three to four months, she will start to recognise night-time and will sleep longer then. By six months, she will probably be taking two to three naps in the day – morning, early afternoon and late afternoon (although experts say not to let a baby nap within three hours of bedtime, or she may have trouble settling for the night).

- By nine to 12 months, most babies take two solid naps a day, in the morning and in the afternoon, each one lasting one to two hours.

- And after 18 months, many babies give up the morning nap and just take one nap in the afternoon – this may continue until they are three or four years old. Some experts say that older children need an afternoon nap too, but for most children naps will stop when other commitments such as nursery or pre-school kick in.

This is a rough guide. Nap needs change as babies reach new developmental milestones. Few babies will follow this pattern exactly – but it will give you an idea of what you might expect. Your baby will do the fine-tuning.

Where can babies nap?

As for the location of your baby's nap – bed, cot or on the move – some experts think that a baby who takes a nap in a cot or quiet room will sleep more deeply and for longer than a baby who naps in a car seat or buggy. So it might be wise to try to engineer that at least a certain proportion of your baby's naps take place at home where she can get this quality sleep.

Some experts advise that babies nap in the same place every day, preferably where they also spend the night, to encourage sleep associations. Others say that napping in a cot or playpen downstairs helps babies to differentiate between long night-time sleep and naps. In my experience most babies 'take' the daytime sleep they need, and will 'top up' if they need to with no adverse effects. Also, setting up a situation where a baby can *only* get to sleep in a quiet, darkened environment isn't practical, and could leave you in a mess if your routine changes and you need to be away from home with your baby for part of the day.

The real 'knack' when it comes to napping seems to be an ability to 'read the signs' – and this is common to all of the four approaches.

Here are some nap tips that are general to any *Baby Sleep Bible* approach:

- Pay attention to your baby's sleep signals. Common signals are rubbing the eyes, staring into space or going 'glassy-eyed', and general fussing and crankiness.

- Maybe keep a record or journal of your baby's sleep signals for a week. You will begin to see patterns which you can base your nap routine around.

- Try giving your baby a nap *before* she gets really tired. By the time she is yawning and lying on the floor whimpering, she is *overtired* and will be difficult to settle. Start your nap-time routine 15–20 minutes before you expect her to show sleep signals, so your baby is already on the road to sleep when she is overcome with tiredness. You have a short window of opportunity when your baby will fall asleep easily and quickly – if you wait too long, she will resist sleep.

- If your baby wakes after 30–45 minutes and whimpers, don't assume she has finished her nap. This is the first stage of the sleep cycle – if left alone, or comforted quietly but *not* picked up – babies will usually go into their second stage which can last up to an hour and a half. Older babies will settle themselves back into their second stage.

- If you are at home, make sure your child is wearing something comfortable and not too light or heavy. Pyjamas or sleepsuits are the obvious choice, but tracksuits or soft trousers are fine too.

- If you can, keep your baby's morning wake-up time and bedtime as consistent as you can – if these are fairly fixed, the naps will fall into place more easily.

What if they won't nap?

There are many reasons why babies might not nap easily. Daytime can be full of distractions. Many babies become overtired and over-stimulated, and parents often miss their 'cues'. Babies under 12 months are also in an active 'discovery' phase and their brains might see exploring the world as more of a priority than resting.

So it's wise not to punish your child for not taking a nap. This is likely to make them dislike napping even more. Instead, giving lots of praise when your baby does wake from a nap will instil positive feelings about it.

You will probably find the solutions for your baby only after some trial and error. So a common-sense approach which takes in a few variations would probably be the best way to go about napping – and a conscious decision not to allow yourself to become stressed by the whole thing. Remember that babies are part of families, and families need to live each day, with all its variations and challenges and twists and turns, as best they can. The beauty of naps is that they *can* be flexible, and whichever approach you are following, you can make nap times fit *your* day.

BACK TO NATURE

The most frequent query parents have about naps and co-sleeping is this: where does she nap during the day? Surely once she can roll, leaving them in an adult bed alone is dangerous? The answer is yes – naps for co-sleeping families do take a little more working out than for families who can just pop baby into their cot exactly the same as at night. But this doesn't mean it is difficult. There are several options open to you.

Top do and don't tips for napping

Leaving a baby alone on a full-height adult bed is clearly not recommended. Even if you are pretty sure your baby is not yet rolling, you can never be absolutely sure when they will suddenly start. Equally, unsupervised babies can become wedged in gaps, or tangled in bedclothes, or shift too near to a radiator or other hazard. Because of this, some Back to Nature parents decide that co-sleeping will only happen at night, or either parent will be napping *with* the baby during the day. All other daytime naps will be taken in a cot or a crib. Others decide that a cot or crib is not worth it just for naps. Or they prefer not to confuse the baby with a mixture of methods. In this case, parents might make sure that the main 'family bed' in the adult bedroom is a low mattress placed directly on the floor, and that the adult bedroom has been thoroughly safety-checked for baby hazards, and then put the baby to bed there on their own.

Other parents buy a small mattress which can be moved around the house for daytime napping – it might be on the floor next to the bed in the adult bedroom, or it might be put on the living room floor, or in a downstairs family room. The advantage of this is that you can cater for your child's needs and for what is going on on a particular day more easily. And you don't have to nap with your child - you can keep an eye on her while you do your downstairs chores or work or read a book. The disadvantage is that if you won't be in the same room, you will have to safety-check that area too in case your baby wakes while you are not looking.

> **"** If I want them to sleep, I usually just look for cues like eye rubbing and lie them down with a dummy to stop fretfulness, or hold them until they drop off. I find next to the stereo or radio works well too.
>
> I encourage them to sleep wherever they want to during the day, but the night-time routine is different and I like to make that distinction. I think it's confusing to 'create' night-time during the day with blackout blinds and it makes them sleep too long. I like to go with the body's natural rhythms. I would never co-sleep during the day unless they are tiny because, again, I think they sleep too long.
>
> Lisa, midwife and mother of Fionn, three, and Bridget, 10 months **"**

Some Back to Nature parents also use baby slings - small babies fall asleep readily in these, snuggled warm next to your body while you move around. In fact, something about the motion and the proximity of your heartbeat seems to act in an almost hypnotic way - Evie used to fall asleep so soundly in a sling that the first few times we did it we panicked and thought she was unconscious. Of course, slings also have the advantage of letting you get on with things while your baby sleeps. Bigger babies get a bit back-breaking and less willing to sleep, though.

Another option is to use a baby swing – these prove very effective in getting babies to sleep. However, try not to rely on them all the time, because they are not practical to cart around if your baby needs to nap at somebody else's house or on holiday, and because they outgrow them quickly and will then have to adapt to a new nap-time routine.

Other tips for Back to Nature nappers are:

- Play some classical music or soft lullabies at a low sound level wherever your baby is sleeping – this relaxes your baby and also acts as a cue that it is sleep time.

- Continue your daily activities while your baby naps – if she get used to the sound of the vacuum cleaner or washing machine or television, she will learn to sleep with background noise and be more adaptable than a baby who demands total silence. Certain kinds of 'white noise' like the Hoover also actually act as a relaxant and help the baby to block out other stimuli and 'let go'.

- Some Back to Nature parents try nursing their baby to sleep on the adult bed. They either stay with their child while they sleep, or work towards being able to move the baby into a cot once asleep. Older toddlers can learn to nurse and then accept being taken to a cot or bed while still awake but drowsy.

❝ Zehra always fell asleep really well if there was some white noise in the background – I used to turn on the hairdryer and she would just drop off.

Maria, mother of Zehra, 12, Ceyda, eight, and Nadia, six **❞**

BY THE CLOCK

By the Clock babies tend to fall into nap-time routines quite well. Not always, but often! And if you are following a particular method such as Ferber or Ford or The Baby Whisperer, they have specific advice on how to follow through your night-time routine into the day, and make sure the entire approach is consistent. For consistency is what it's all about with By the Clock approaches. It's no good putting in lots of work to achieve your night-time routine and then letting it all slide during the day – your baby will be confused and disrupted. What is also common to most of these approaches is that they encourage babies to learn to fall asleep for naps without sleeping 'props' such as the use of motion (rocking) or sucking.

The beauty of a nap-time approach which is structured is that it gives your baby that thing that most babies crave – routine, and the security of knowing what is coming next.

It also encourages you to study your child and work out what times of the day she is usually tired, hungry or wanting to play – and to work with that. Even if you don't want to follow a rigid daily routine, it helps to have certain things occur at roughly the same time every day – this will keep you and your baby on track.

> **❝** Stanley and Poppy are both good nappers. We started the routine early – a story, a darkened room, the same strictness as at bedtime. It might limit your flexibility during the day, but it gives you happy children!
>
> Alex, father of Stanley, four, and Poppy, 19 months **❞**

Top do and don't tips for napping

A general By the Clock approach might be:

- Follow a nap-time routine which is similar to your bedtime one, but condensed. Maybe read one short book, or sing a lullaby and have a cuddle. Signal to your baby that it is time to nap by closing curtains or blinds and turning off the lights. Try not to chat with your baby – keep everything still and calm.

- Let your baby doze off in the same place if possible. She can nap in the car or pushchair, but if you are at home, always use the same spot. If she goes to a nursery or childminder, have her nap in the same place on home days or weekends.

- Put your baby in her cot at the first sign that she is tired, but when she is still awake. Try not to rock or feed her to sleep or she will come to rely on this and won't learn to fall asleep alone.

- You can offer a comforter or blankie if this helps her settle by herself. My children both had one – Evie had Blue Bear, who is still hanging on in there despite being distinctly tatty now, and Charlie has Ducky who forms an integral part of his 'bottom in the air' sleeping pose, and gets tucked underneath his tummy. Don't worry if she doesn't 'bond' with your chosen comforter – babies will often rather single-mindedly attach to something of their own choosing, such as a muslin or even one of your T-shirts. Charlie ignored the plush bear we got him at birth and decided Ducky, an incidental purchase, was 'the one'.

- Try not to keep your baby up late at night unless unavoidable. Most By the Clock approaches rely on a consistent timetable. If you approach naps with the same calm determination as bedtime, your baby will feel comforted and secure. If you fall asleep with her on your bed, or change the rules, your baby will feel unsettled and may think nap times are an 'optional extra' rather than an integral part of her day.

- Older babies and toddlers sometimes resist naps. Try to insist they have a 'quiet time' in their cot anyway, with maybe a soft toy or a board book. This kind of play is different from normal play – although they're not sleeping, they will at least have time to unwind and recharge. Often they will chat for a while and then fall asleep in spite of themselves. An advantage of having a cot in a nursery is that the cot keeps them contained, whereas it is difficult to encourage co-sleepers to play alone in one spot.

- It isn't necessary that just because your baby is sleeping in a cot in their own room, everything has to be silent. Background noise from downstairs will comfort your baby and ensure that she can sleep in different circumstances, rather than being reliant on a 'hear-a-pin-drop' environment.

- You *can* leave the house on a By the Clock routine. Babies will come to no harm napping while out and about. Just try to make the opportunity for your baby's nap to happen at a time she would normally nap at home – for instance, if your baby usually needs a nap at 2pm, and you have to go shopping, time your journey to the shopping centre for around 2pm so she will get a nap in the car before you get there. Or, if you know your baby drops off well in a buggy, aim to leave slightly earlier, and get to the shopping centre for 2pm so she can nap while you push her round.

Picturing the day

A different way of getting an older baby or toddler to cooperate in a daily routine is to create a daily 'picture schedule' for them. Take a digital picture of your child sleeping, or reading a story with a parent, or brushing their teeth or having milk or a bath. Include nap times and pre-nap activities. Then paste them onto a piece of card for your child to visually understand what her day is all about. It's an appealing way of providing structure and predictability and presenting it in a way that your baby can understand and anticipate. You can even ask day nursery staff to help you create a similar one for days she is there.

By the Clockers can feel ever so slightly smug when it comes to nap times, because the chances are that they have already established good sleep associations and an ability on the baby's part to settle themselves well. Half the job is done. Just keep up the same calm, structured approach and your baby will be napping like a natural.

66 The 'quiet time' approach can work really well for older toddlers as it gives parents some much needed rest during a busy day. I always maintained that nap times are for the grownups' benefit! Having said that, breastfeeding mothers really should try to put their feet up for a short while during a busy day. Rest improves the quantity and quality of breast milk.

Sara Warren, midwife

99

FLEXI-SLEEPING

Napping for Flexi-Sleepers needs to be as adaptable as possible. This does not mean that there is no room for a little of that structure and routine which is so important for your baby's sense of security. It just means that you have to be a bit clever about factoring in the nap times and keeping some consistency in the chaos. Remember that 'chain of constants'? Time to add a couple more in again!

66 Daytimes have always been a bit of a battle. She just does not like sleeping, during the day, in her cot. When we put her in her cot for a daytime nap, more often than not we have to leave her to cry herself to sleep, which is, well... difficult! When tired, however, she will normally drop off within five minutes in the car, and after a little bit longer in her pushchair. Unfortunately

neither of these cases mean me or Jo can have a nap, buy hey ho! The price of a happy child is tired parents.

Dan, father of Talise, nine months

Top do and don't tips for napping

Obviously, you will still be sticking to all the usual bedtime 'rituals', but paring them down for a daytime nap. These include the familiar nightwear, comforter, lullabies and book, the 'special words' and cues, and the sharing of this information with anyone else who regularly looks after your child. However, in addition to this, you could encourage your baby to feel comfortable napping in different locations – as long as all that other familiar stuff remains constant.

You can start this when your baby is quite young, by moving her around the house for naps. Use an easy-to-carry Moses basket or carry-cot, perhaps with a sturdy stand, and alter the location – one day in the adult bedroom, the next day the nursery, the next day the living room, then in a play room, and then perhaps by the back door in a pram if it's a warm day, and occasional visits to friends' houses with naps built in too.

Because I am a childminder, George was always used to napping in the midst of a lot of noise, which is a good idea – don't create a silent environment that you can't re-create all the time. He was an 'on the move baby' – he would just sleep in the car or the buggy. He had to be.

Nikki, childminder and mother of George, six

As your baby gets older, she will be less portable, but you could still encourage naps at grandma's house, or friends' houses on an occasional basis. If you know you will be sending your child to a childminder or nursery, or that she will be spending regular time with other family members, you can build it up *before* this kicks in, so that by the time she has to cope with it, she is fully secure.

Another tip for babies who will have to take naps at a day nursery or a childminder is to introduce early the idea of background noise. The noise of other children and adults will come as a shock to a baby who has been used to taking naps in a quiet house, so turn on the television or play some music, or get some younger members of your extended family to come around at weekends at baby's nap times.

Once your baby is in day care, check the nursery's schedule – you can try to follow their nap timings on the days your baby is with you at home, so that the disruption is kept to a minimum.

> **❝** If parents adopt the 'Shhhh don't wake the baby!' attitude, the chances are they'll have a child who wakes at the slightest disturbance. Far better to get babies used to being able to sleep with some background noise.
>
> Sara Warren, midwife **❞**

Napping 'constants'

The first is the use of a **nap-time whiteout**. This means removing as many stimuli as possible from your baby's immediate environment just before sleep. For 'out and about' babies the cheapest and easiest way of doing this is to use a white muslin cloth, the sort you use to wipe up your baby's gunk. Keep a clean one with you, and give duplicates to other adults who care for your baby. When she goes to sleep, the muslin can be draped somewhere near the baby (but not where it can cover her face or get entangled). If your baby is napping in a car seat or buggy, the cloth can be draped over the hood and/or handle. The baby will only see this white area, and it will 'let go' and allow sleep to come. I have friends who did this, and their baby's ability to 'switch off' like a light wherever they happened to be was the envy of all of us. A variation on this is to stand with your baby in your arms, looking backwards over your shoulder at a white wall. You can do this for a few minutes before laying her down. Staff at a nursery, or a childminder, could do this too.

The second is a **small-sized soft fleecy blanket**. You can add this to your baby's 'kit' of sleep tools. It will be used wherever your baby has a nap, and can be added in at bedtime as well – older babies and children who sleep in a bed can either use it as part of their bedclothes, or have it rolled up like a bolster beside them. Now sleep with the blanket for a couple of nights to give it a distinctive, comforting smell. Then you need to fold the blanket over your baby's knees whenever she sleeps. Try to choose a blanket that is fairly lightweight – then it can be used in summer too, and simply folded double in colder months.

66 I would often use a baby swing for daytime naps, and they would sleep really well in that while I used the time to work from home.

Jo, mother of Archie, six, and
Charlotte, four 99

If you are worried that your child by now has several items which need to travel with her when she goes to other houses or carers, you could buy a very small child's suitcase or bag in which they all go as a matter of course whenever your baby is away from you. If you have it all set up and ready to go, you are less likely to forget something or feel stressed trying to gather it together. A little preparation is a small price in exchange for your baby's peace of mind when Flexi-Sleeping.

MULTIPLE MADNESS

If you thought that getting two or more sleepy babies to go to sleep at night was a challenge, try doing the same when they are awake and buzzing during the day! The irony is that, while having twins or multiples makes it harder to get nap times right, parents of twins and multiples probably need their babies to nap well more than any other parents! You will be relying on grabbing short daytime naps yourself to make up for interrupted nights and general exhaustion. Physical exhaustion leads to emotional stress and feelings of being unable to cope, so it is essential that your babies nap in the day.

Your nap-time approach with twins or multiples will depend largely on whether they are sleeping in the same bed or room, or whether they have separate rooms. If they are sleeping separately, you could follow the same advice as for By the Clock parents – keeping to a calm, consistent schedule and instigating a short nap-time routine similar to their bedtime one. If, however, your babies are sharing a sleeping space, that's where the fun starts – especially when they are old enough to climb out of a cot or are in beds.

> **66** Whenever possible I would put the babies down in their cots. This was definitely what I preferred. If they had their naps in the buggy or the car that was OK but I always tried to get them down in their cots for their lunchtime sleep. They always slept in the day with the curtains drawn, door closed, holding their blankies.
>
> Callie, mother of Lily, four, and James and Sophia, two **99**

Top do and don't tips for napping

The main challenge with nap times is that your babies will be less tired than at bedtime – and will have a willing little co-conspirator to help them get into mischief. If they have their naps in a room with lots of fun things to do as well as each other's company, your babies will probably not be getting the quiet transition time that helps them move from 'sleepy' to 'asleep'. As mentioned before, when setting up rooms for multiples in general, try to keep the area a quiet, relatively toy-free space. This doesn't mean no toys – it just means having toy boxes or trunks or storage where they can be put away for sleep. A darkened room is better than a stimulating space.

If you can set aside a period – say, half-an-hour – of 'down time' for your babies before they are expected to actually go to sleep, this will help them wind down.

It will also let you see which of your babies actually *needs* to sleep at that time – you might find both fall asleep, or perhaps one will sleep while the other busies herself, playing quietly and simply having a break from the day. If they can co-exist on this basis, there is no need to do anything else. But if the awake twin disturbs the twin who needs to sleep, or they both need sleep at widely different times of the day, then you might have to create separate nap-time sleeping areas for them, even if they come back together to sleep at night.

The best approach if you need to do this is to let the poorer sleeper stay in the normal bedroom, and find an alternative sleeping area in your room or downstairs for the better sleeper, who will adapt more easily.

> ❝ Naps – those were the days! We were quite strict about it – when you have twins, you need to catch up on sleep yourself. They both napped until they started pre-school.
>
> Matt, father of Luke and Perry, seven ❞

In addition, be aware that nap-time is a time when many accidents happen to children – and more so with twins and multiples, who tend to egg each other on, encourage each other in their exploration, and who can help each other reach things and climb where single children may not. Also, this is often a time when the main caregiver is also taking a much-needed nap – and so won't have one ear open for trouble. Parents of twins have reported nap-time adventures including: climbing out of a window or getting out of the house; emptying drawers and climbing on unsteady furniture; decorating rooms with talcum powder or nappy rash cream; decorating the room with the contents of their nappies; balancing between pieces of furniture; peeling off wallpaper or friezes; and becoming wedged beneath beds or furniture.

One way to combat this is to use a baby monitor, and place your end right beside your ear if you are going to nap yourself. Video monitors are also good. And so are willing helpers who will agree to pop round and supervise for an hour while you sleep. It isn't helpful to punish your children for not taking a nap. This is likely to make them dislike napping even more. Instead provide verbal praise when your toddlers wake from a nap.

In fact, willing helpers are often the difference between coping and despair for parents of multiples. Take any offers you get.

And for those times when you are alone, think 'clear and secure' – clear all unnecessary debris, toys and furniture, and secure with stair gates, furniture wall bolts and window locks. It might make you feel more of a prison officer than a parent, but at least you will be a well-slept one!

SAFETY AT NAP TIME

An extremely important 'and finally' in this chapter is this: safety. Whichever approach you choose to take, remember that your baby's safety is paramount.

Around 300 babies under the age of one die each year in the UK from cot death, or sudden infant death syndrome (SIDS). Although parents these days are only too aware of this and take all due precautions to minimise the risks when they put their babies to sleep at night, many of us forget or let things slide during daytime naps.

A study published in the *International Journal of Epidemiology* and carried out by experts from Bristol University, Newcastle's Royal Victoria Infirmary and the Nuffield Institute for Health found that the overwhelming majority of cot deaths – 83% – happened at night. But of those that happened during the day, 75% were when babies were left in rooms unattended. The study, which was carried out over three years and studied 1,625 children, 325 of whom died of SIDS, also found that one in four of the babies left alone in a room without an adult had bedclothes over their heads, compared with one in 10 where a parent was present. The study also showed that death could happen very quickly – among the daytime deaths, 38% were seen to be alive 30 minutes before they were found dead, and 9% just 10 minutes before they were found.

This information isn't intended to frighten you – just to remind you to take as much care over safety in the day as you would at night. If you are going to leave your child in a room alone for their nap – whether on a mattress in your room or in a cot in her nursery – sleep her on her back. Keep the room temperature to around 18 degrees Celsius, and if it is hotter, remove some layers of clothing. Consider using a baby sleeping bag with an appropriate tog rating for the time of year – these shouldn't ride up and cover the baby's head, even if they wriggle. And remove all hazards such as pillows, cot bumpers, large stuffed toys and any dangling leads or cords.

Finally, check in regularly and keep some background noise on. Don't worry that this will disturb your baby – it may make them sleep slightly less deeply, but many experts feel that this is a good thing because babies who sleep very deeply might be less able to rouse themselves if they have a breathing delay or other trauma.

If you are not leaving your baby alone but intend to nap with her, you still need to take precautions. It isn't advisable to sleep next to your baby if you have been taking medication or drugs or alcohol, and it is recommended that you *never* fall asleep with a baby on a sofa. Naps might be more flexible than night-time sleeps, but they need just as much thought and care – so keep your baby's safety in mind whatever the clock says.

> 66 I think it's natural for every parent to worry about SIDS. I was especially nervous at nap times when I was doing bits and bobs around the house and could get distracted. I was very nervous for the first three months, but after that, I calmed down a bit, but still following every safety precaution I should.
>
> Sarah, mother of Nicholas, six months 99

66 It's all too easy for tired parents to put babies or small children down for naps without paying attention to the environment. Those extra few seconds checking the bed and room for potential hazards can literally save lives, to say nothing of protecting a room from the aforementioned potential for toddler vandalism!

Sara Warren, midwife 99

5

Sleep Away from Home

" Life is something that happens when you can't get to sleep. **"**

Fran Lebowitz

B y now you have got yourself and your baby well on the way to successful sleeping, both day and night. You have followed your chosen approach, and have found what works for you. But would it still work – if you had to do it all away from home?

It's a sad irony that many parents dream of – would almost chew their own arm off for – a holiday after they have regained consciousness following the severe blow to the head that is childbirth and the early baby days. Yet when they finally head off to wherever they have been dreaming of, equipped with travel cot, mosquito net and countless other baby travel paraphernalia, their touching optimism turns to despair and a stinging sense of the unfairness of it all when baby refuses to sleep. At all.

Babies who at home are content to cuddle up beside you and fall asleep suddenly find that in a strange new place, they need their own space. Babies who are used to the calm of their own cot and nursery struggle when they have to share a room with siblings, or everyone has to bed down in one cramped hotel room. And to cap it all, even the most flexible of routines are challenged by long car, train or plane journeys, fitting in siestas or evening meals out as a family, or worst of all – different time zones.

Even if you decide to play it safe and holiday in the UK, the change of location alone can be enough to disrupt things. The relatively unambitious undertaking of a day trip to see family or friends can end in tears – both yours and your baby's – if your baby cannot sleep. So what's the solution? Is it even possible to attempt travel with a baby? And how do you make any of the *Baby Sleep Bible* approaches work when you are on the move?

Baby travel tips

There are some helpful things you can do to ease your little traveller's experience of time zone changes, no matter which approach you follow:

- Before you go – if travelling to a time zone which is a few hours back, such as America, adjust sleeping times a little later for a few days before departure. If going east, move sleep times a little earlier. Small changes such as a 15-minute shift won't disturb your baby, but when added up will make an hour or more's difference.

- While in transit, try to go to bed at the same time as your baby. If you are with your partner or other family member, take it in turns to do 'shifts' to deal with the night, or with very early morning waking.

- Once you have arrived, aim to put your baby to bed on the first night yourself rather than someone else. Keep everything, including yourself, as familiar as possible.

- Give feeds or meals at their usual intervals, regardless of what time it is.

- If your baby wants to sleep in the car, train or plane – the motion often makes babies sleep longer than usual – don't worry about it. It's ok to encourage this even if it goes against your usual schedule. One long nap will make little difference in the long run, and will probably be 'cancelled out' by the general travel exhaustion.

- Check in early, or take advantage of 'priority' boarding schemes where families board first. You can also ask if there are any spare seats so your child can lie down.

- Keep your buggy with you until you board – the airline staff will take it at the steps or entry gantry, and stow it in the hold. This way, your baby can nap at the airport.

- Dress babies and children in soft, well-worn clothes with easy fastenings. These can then double up as pyjamas and minimise disruption to a dozy baby. Take spares.

- Reserve a 'sky cot' or bassinet if you can. Ask if you can take car seats on board – some airlines allow this, and not only is it a good safety option, but a baby will often sleep better in this familiar environment.

- Travel during the night if you can. 'Red-eye' flights can work well if they coincide with your baby's usual sleep time. Pull the window shade down and minimise your own noise and activity. For short-haul holiday flights, you could synchronise a flight with an afternoon nap.

- Remember that the more time zones you cross, the longer it will take your baby to adjust. Use cues to keep your baby awake even if their internal clock thinks it is bedtime – one good cue is sunlight. Let them play and feed where it is sunny and light.

- Avoid, if you can, taking your baby anywhere where there is a dramatic change in climate or altitude – this will make her ability to adapt even harder.

- If you have to go to a very dry place, take a vaporiser or humidifier for the room she will be sleeping in.

- Do remember to reverse the whole process when it's time to go home!

BACK TO NATURE

In many respects, Back to Nature families usually find it easier to adapt to sleeping away from home, because they are already used to sleeping in close proximity. Many will share a bed, or at least be used to sleeping next to each other on separate mattresses. This adapts perfectly to sharing a hotel room, or tent or self-catering space. It also means that your baby will continue to be in close proximity to you during her trip, which will minimise much of the anxiety small children feel when in unfamiliar surroundings or coping with a new routine.

There are still some things you can do to make sure your co-sleeping baby adapts well to her 'away from home' location.

> " Routines change when away from home and I always let the kids know it's temporary! It usually goes out the window to some degree and that's fine. I always bring their own bedding and usual toys to help them adapt. I find they sleep great in hotel rooms because they know you're close by and no-one's going to work! "
>
> Lisa, mother of Fionn, three, and Bridget, 10 months

Beating the travel blues

- For car and long-distance train travel, you can buy a lightweight, zip-up blanket for baby to cosy up in on her seat. These are not full-thickness sleeping bags, just novelty products often with character designs on them, for instance Disney does a range of 'Snuggle Sacs'. They can be worn over the legs and lower body even in a car seat, and are especially comforting when travelling at night. These can be used also for plane travel – roll them up tightly to fit in your child's hand luggage, then unroll for dozing on a seat, or across your lap, or even down on the floor by your feet if the seatbelt signs are off. Some parents try to get bulkhead seats, and older children can then snuggle in front of your feet by the wall.

- If you are bottle feeding or taking bottled expressed milk, check the airline regulations in advance for restrictions on liquids. But if you are breastfeeding, you might want to nurse during take-offs and landings because the sucking motion will help your baby's ears pop. Some mothers put their smaller babies in a sling or soft baby carrier, which allows for discrete breastfeeding, and also lets you get up to go to the loo without waking a sleeping baby. Most airlines are sympathetic to a mother nursing during a flight, but try to wear easy-access clothing and perhaps strategically drape a muslin cloth if you are sharing a row with someone you don't know.

- Once at your destination, you will need to decide where your child will sleep. A very small baby might sleep well in a 'nest' which sits next to you on the adult bed – you might consider this if the bed is higher than your own at home, or has a gap next to a wall that you cannot easily fill, or is narrower than you are used to.

- Another product you could use is the inflatable bolster – this will pack up small in your luggage, but inflates very quickly and sits under the sheet to provide a secure 'edge' to your bed. There are also co-sleeping mats with attached soft bolsters for those who have more luggage room.

- If you are used to your child sleeping in the same room but not in the same bed, you also have options. A baby used to a Moses basket or crib might feel comfortable in a portable carry-cot, which will double as a pram for outings.

- A baby used to a 'sidecar' arrangement will benefit from the travel versions of these – just like travel cots, but with a folding fourth side. These are also useful as playpens for accommodation with hazards such as steep steps or unguarded swimming pools.

- An older child used to sleeping on a mattress next to you can be accommodated by either removing a mattress from a spare single bed and placing it next to your bed, or, if there will be no spare beds, by bringing along a roll-up bed roll or light mattress. A good emergency bed is a blow-up lilo covered in towels and then a fitted sheet – although these can be a bit hot and sticky for a long holiday.

Remember that however comfortable your baby is sleeping with you at home, a change of location might bring about unexpected reactions.

If you are going to a hot place, your baby may feel uncomfortable in the heat and may struggle to settle next to you, and it may be best to put her in a pram or carry-cot. And even if your baby sleeps well with you, she might wake early and go wandering – so remember to make sure doors are secured and heavy or dangerous objects are removed.

Back to Nature families tend to have a flexible approach to holiday accommodation though – so try to organise sleep away from home with your normal cosy calmness and you should have a stress-free break.

❝ I have never had a problem with mine, and we regularly go away for two to three nights in hotels. We may go to bed later at times, but as long as we are with them, they are fine. And we have never come home to a problematic disrupted routine.

Make sure they are tired out, well-fed, and talk about the next day and the need for everyone to sleep so that we can all enjoy another great day. Bribe if necessary, and let them know that if they get too loud we could all be asked to leave!

Dalvinder, mother of Amber five, India, three, and Jasmine, 11 months **❞**

BY THE CLOCK

By the Clock families, used to the ordered routine of separate sleeping spaces and clearly delineated 'baby time' and 'adult time', may feel rather apprehensive about the more relaxed and less spacious aspects of holidays and travel.

That's not to say that your normal approach is destined to crumble into disorder and sleeplessness once you leave home. Although some parents swear that there is 'no such thing as a holiday with a baby', there are certainly things you can do to adapt your normal routine into a holiday format – and indeed, the fact that you have spent so much time helping your baby to self-comfort, and have nurtured positive sleep associations, will stand you in good stead.

The trick to helping By the Clock babies sleep well away from home is preparation.

Since your baby will be very used to her own cot or crib, you have two options: either you will need to take quite a bit of gear with you, or you will need to figure out how to replace it once you have reached your destination. You may also need to reassure your baby that her normal routine hasn't gone completely out of the window.

> We often go on holiday either in the UK or in northern France and drive there — it makes it a lot easier to take extra things with you that help you set up your routine away from home. People tease us for making life difficult for ourselves by taking too much, but actually it means that once you're there, you feel much more relaxed and able to enjoy it.
>
> Gill, mother of Stanley, four, and Poppy, 19 months

Beating the travel blues

You will find it helpful to prepare for your holiday a week *before* you leave. You might be intending to use a cot provided by a hotel or holiday company. If so, call now to check what kind of cot it will be, whether it is suitable for your baby, and what the dimensions are (some provide travel cots that are more like playpens, others use continental sized cots which are larger than standard). This will enable you to decide if you need to take a travel cot of your own – and if not, what size sheets will fit it.

The sheets are important. Not only do many places not provide bedding at all, but even if they do, your child will feel much more reassured if she is sleeping on a familiar texture with familiar smells. Take a fitted sheet, and perhaps a flat cot sheet in case the fitted one won't stretch. And consider taking one that isn't freshly washed – it will smell all the more comforting!

If you will be using the cot provided, please look at the end of this chapter for important safety advice. If you will be taking your own or travel cot with you, then follow these simple steps:

1. The week before you travel, put up your travel cot downstairs in the living room. Put a couple of interesting toys in it – perhaps one old familiar one and one new one. Let your baby approach it, play in it and perhaps doze in it for the odd nap.

   After a couple of days, start to move the travel cot around the house. Put it in the kitchen or playroom, then take it upstairs to your bedroom. Make it a visually familiar object.

2. Then move it into your child's bedroom, alongside her normal cot. Aim not to sleep her in it at night-time yet, but let her explore it and use it for naps.

3. Finally, for the two nights before you go, follow your baby's normal bedtime routine but lay her in the travel cot instead of the normal cot. Make sure all other bedtime objects such as comforters and sheets are the same.

4. You should find that, on arrival in your travel destination, your baby will accept this travel cot more readily, even if it is in a shared room or a hotel room with you.

5. If your older toddler is in a bed already, try taking a familiar pillow, or one of the 'Sleep Sacs' recommended in the Back to Nature section, for comfort. Even a favourite blanket might do the trick.

Whether your baby is a small newborn or an older toddler, the first rule of helping her to sleep on holiday is to make the environment as similar to the one back home as you can. You have done your best with the cot or bed – so now you have to think about the rest of her sleeping space.

When we travel, I always pack one bedtime book each for Evie and Charlie, so that we can sit together and read a well-known story at bedtime. They also have Blue Bear and Ducky, their comforters.

If you use blackout blinds at home, you can buy travel versions which push against the sides of windows with suction cups. Or you can simply take some pegs and rig up a dense blanket at the window.

Other things you can do are:

- During that week before you go, play a soothing CD at bedtime every night, and play the same CD (or perhaps a song from an MP3 player and speakers) at holiday bedtimes too.

- Take a familiar music box or musical lullaby player.

- Keep your bedtime ritual the same, even if it happens later in the evening.

If it is important to you to maintain your baby's regular bedtime, or at least keep it relatively early, think in advance about the type of accommodation you are choosing. Does it have an outside space where the adults can sit and eat or chat? A terrace or balcony? Unless you are prepared to go to bed at 7pm with your babies, one hotel room between all of you is not much fun when you are restricted to watching television on mute, reading silently and whispering under the covers – self-catering accommodation is often more flexible and spacious.

66 Don't do hotels – unless it's one of those expensive family-oriented ones! Self-catering is much more flexible, and booking an apartment with a separate room for the children makes all the difference. Also, take your baby monitor – you can use it normally to listen to them fall asleep, and we sometimes use it backwards (switch the ends) so they can hear us chatting on the balcony and feel reassured we are near.

Tom, father of Rebecca, eight, Ashley, five, and Vincent, three 99

The advantage you will have as a By the Clock family is that you will all be secure in knowing that you have found a routine that works. Don't feel anxious about transplanting it – if you allow for just a little flexibility while away you will probably find that your secure baby will adapt with aplomb. And most parents find that, on returning home, their baby slots right back into the original routine without so much as the blink of an eye. Or a bedtime wail.

FLEXI-SLEEPING

If there is one baby who is set up to deal blithely with a change of locations, late bedtimes and unfamiliar objects and people, it is your baby. Everything you have done so far has set you up for a globetrotting baby adventurer. All you have to do is carry on those same approaches while you are away. As long as you don't lose sight of your 'chain of constants', your baby will probably see no difference between that hotel room or apartment and going to nursery or to grandma's house.

> **"** George has always adapted really well to being away from home, because he has had to be so flexible at home. From the moment he was born, I've never stopped doing anything I did before. He just 'joined' my life. He's sociable, and it has never bothered him to go anywhere or to be left with any other adult.
>
> Nikki, childminder and mother of George, six **"**

Beat the travel blues

Take your arsenal of Flexi-Sleeping weapons along with you, as much as is practical. It may seem a nuisance when you are trying to pack the entire contents of your house into a few bags with the proportions of a Barbie luggage set, but you will very much welcome those items if you can manage it.

Remember that, if your child is over two years old, or you have paid for an aeroplane seat for a younger baby, then that child has a baggage allowance too. She doesn't have to actually have her own suitcase, if you are worried about how to carry everything – it goes by weight, so you can simply distribute her weight allowance between the adults' bags.

Also, a buggy and, depending on the airline, a car seat, can go in addition to your allowance. You might also swing a travel cot. And many of your child's sleep-time essentials, such as her comforter and blanket, will need to be with you anyway, so these can be rolled tightly and taken in hand luggage.

> **"** Doing holidays is really hard when it's just you, with one pair of hands. Luckily Sasha is so adaptable, she has always been quite laid back about it all. My best tip is to get one of those baby sleeping bags – but you can get ones with slits in the back so they can be used in a car seat or buggy, and the harness goes through the slits. It means they can doze off and be put straight into their cot or bed if you are late back.
>
> Kim, mother of Sasha, two **"**

Other tips to encourage adaptability are:

- Take a great piece of handy Flexi-Sleeping equipment – which is also fun and useful for any baby – a lightweight UV sun tent or cabana. Not only is this a fun place to play indoors, and also a great way to protect your baby from the sun on the beach or by the pool, it is also a great place for a nap. You can buy baby-sized ones or ones that the whole family can fit in – deck it out with a couple of soft beach towels plus your child's 'whiteout muslin' and other nap-time gear, and your baby can enjoy a nap while you read or snooze beside them. Remember to apply sun cream though, even in the shade.

- If your child especially enjoys her little rituals and would like to add a special, temporary holiday one, why not buy a special 'sunshine teddy' or 'holiday dolly' in a local shop and introduce it into your child's sleep routine? (Check toys for safety, loose ribbons and bows or small parts.) Or think of a fun daily routine – 'every time I go to sleep, I can put a special shell in my bucket when I wake up. When I have 10 shells, Daddy will take me for an ice cream'.

- If you are going to be travelling at night, or will be staying out late for a meal, put babies in pyjamas or even a baby sleeping bag so they can be lifted into their cot or a bed with minimal disturbance at the end of the night. Or, if they are dressed from the day, just let them sleep in their clothes for one night.

You can always tell any holiday 'carers' about your child's rituals and 'constants' – this might be a hotel babysitter, or a member of staff at a play club, or simply other adults you are holidaying with. Nobody will mind helping keep your 'chain' together if it means they are holidaying with a happy, peaceful and settled baby.

> ❝ I think you have to be brave and travel to wherever you want to and understand that children do adapt very easily. As adults you are more conscious of time zones and what it is doing to your body clock, in my experience children adapt to the new routine very easily. Trying to keep them awake and occupied on your first day until bedtime when they fall into a happy and exhausted sleep normally means a good night's sleep for everyone.
>
> Maxine, mother of Marnie, 10, and Freddy, four ❞

One final bit of advice is that, as a Flexi-Sleeping family, you are likely to value your holiday freedom as much as possible and will very likely be successful at managing late evenings and meal times out with your children. But when you do get home, try to create even a short period of 'wind-down' time. Ask other adults to sit and chat quietly for a short time while you start your bedtime ritual – it is hard to expect your baby to just pop off to sleep when she can see and hear everybody else running around having fun and making noise. Completely worn-out children do not settle well – if they have had a siesta or a good daytime nap, and just before bed have had their usual time with stories and music and 'special words', they will relax into their usual sleepy sense of security.

MULTIPLE MADNESS

Obviously, wherever you go with twins or multiples, and by whichever method of transport, you are coping with at least double the trouble. Not to mention double the baby gear, double the upset sleep schedules, double the crankiness and double the amount of feeding, carrying and napping to be done in transit.

> 66 Any parents of twins brave enough to attempt a holiday abroad are probably either slightly mad or just incredibly capable types of which the rest of us are in awe! If you can afford it I'd recommend taking an extra, trusted, adult along as a holiday nanny to allow parents some much needed time off.
>
> Sara Warren, midwife 99

> 66 Take Granny! Or team up for a villa holiday with another family with children — it might be madness, but there are more hands on deck to help out, and the children entertain themselves more.
>
> Matt, father of Luke and Perry, seven 99

Beating the travel blues

The first thing you have to do if you are planning to travel by plane is make lots of enquiries ahead of your departure. Things you need to consider are:

- What will the adult/baby ratio be? The Civil Aviation Authority states that there is no general rule regarding the number of children one adult can be responsible for on a flight. It is up to the individual airlines to make their own rules. But – many airlines do have a rule saying that they cannot have more than one baby-in-arms in a single row. This is because there is only one 'extra' oxygen mask in each row, so in an emergency, one baby or adult would be left without a mask. The advice is that adults always put their own masks on before helping children with masks, because if an adult passes out they cannot help a baby. If your airline makes you and your partner sit separately with a baby each, ask to be seated directly behind or in front of your partner, or across the aisle from each other, so that you can pass changing bags, food and other belongings more easily.

- Some airlines will allow an adult to travel with two babies if at least one of the babies is in an approved car seat. Car seats have to be next to the window – another reason you will probably have to sit on different rows.

- Don't rely on airline staff being willing to hold a baby for you while you get up, or feed the other. Many airlines forbid their staff from holding infants for insurance reasons.

- To encourage sleep while on the move, consider flying at nap times. Also consider using soft slings if you are travelling with a partner – you can hold one baby each, and swap for breastfeeding if necessary. And if you doze off yourself, your baby won't fall off your lap.

- Allow lots of extra time for check-in. Take your buggy with you so your babies can nap, and check it in when boarding the plane – but consider swapping your usual bulky double buggy for two lightweight single ones. This may seem like extra equipment, but it means that while on holiday, both adults can do separate activities and take a baby each – shopping, going for a stroll. Also, in many destinations, double buggies are difficult to manoeuvre through narrow doorways, or down narrow cobbled streets. Singles are lighter, neater and easier to steer.

Flying buggies

Although it is now common practice to allow parents to take buggies right up to the aeroplane steps, their fate at the 'other end' is less consistent – some airlines greet you with the buggy at the other end, but others let the buggies come out with all the other hold luggage. And trying to carry two babies and your hand luggage to the baggage reclaim hall and then finding all your hold luggage with no buggy is no picnic. Ask in advance what their policy is, and whether you can be met at the other end.

Once you reach your accommodation, you must decide where the babies will sleep. If you are co-sleeping, consider the inflatable bolsters or the travel 'sidecar' cots mentioned in the Back to Nature section. Or move mattresses onto the floor for toddlers.

If you require cots, read the safety advice below. Some companies will provide double the baby equipment if you book in advance – indeed some companies specialise in it. See www.totstofrance. co.uk for one that provides equipment and tailor-made French holidays for families with twins.

It is simply impossible to replicate every piece of equipment you have at home. Thankfully you don't need to. Things that can be rented or hired in many countries include:

- Cribs and cots
- Highchairs
- Playpens
- Buggies
- Car seats
- Stair gates
- Large play items

Some internet companies will also buy essential supplies of food, nappies, baby formula and other paraphernalia for you and have it waiting in your accommodation on arrival.

Remember to keep to your babies' nap-time and bedtime rituals.

If possible, make a room or an area of your accommodation darker and quiet. If your twins are used to separate sleeping spaces but you don't have enough bedrooms each, consider putting one baby in with each parent, or one baby in a bedroom and the other in a living area. For nap times, if their schedules are upset or they won't settle, try strolls in the buggies, or naps in a cabana outside. Relax the rules while you are away – if you can pull this off, every other parent in the world will be in awe of you. Don't be hard on yourself for getting creative on the sleep front. Anything that helps them catch up on their rest will give you and them a better break – and when you get home again, you will realise that normal routine that seemed so chaotic compared to families with single babies is actually quite streamlined after all!

> **"** I try to stick to the night-time routine when away from home and always keep their muslins handy during the day if they want to nap in the buggy or car. Gran has two travel cots at her home so I do put them down for their daytime sleep there.
>
> They nearly always settle down to night sleep when they are away from home – we keep the milk, story, sleep routine when possible. I will always take a few favourite toys for their cots and show them their rooms beforehand and talk them through it.
>
> Callie, mother of Lily, four, and James and Sophia, two **"**

SAFETY AWAY FROM HOME

Lastly, bear in mind that your safety antennae need to be on high alert when you travel away from home. It is tempting, when somewhere warm and relaxing, to let your guard down or somehow feel that nothing bad could possibly happen in such a lovely place – but in fact, accidents are more likely to happen because of the sheer unfamiliarity of the surroundings and the fact that you haven't evolved a safety routine like you have at home. And people are people, whether they live in hot or cold countries – there are nice people, and there are dangerous people.

Don't let your baby wander out of sight, or leave them outside a shop in a buggy. Put an ID wristband on them, with your mobile phone number on it, your holiday address, and perhaps your travel company details.

On the sleep front, extra precautions you can take are:

- Do a 'once over' safety check of your accommodation on the first full day. Check steps, unguarded staircases, sharp edges, table corners, water temperature, balcony heights, unfenced swimming pools, unlockable windows on ground floors. Some things you can move or alter – hotels or self-catering companies might provide you with a stair gate, for instance. And you will at least be more aware of the ones you can't change, and fix up an arrangement where at least one adult is supervising at all times.

- Consider packing a travel stair gate. You can control your baby's movements more easily. Unless your baby is still at the pre-crawling or shuffling stage, she will move when you least expect it – you will relax more if you can restrict access to certain areas.

- Maybe take a few cupboard locks. The double locks don't need screwing to the cupboard door, they just lock over the door handles – and keep an inquisitive early riser away from bathroom toiletries and kitchen cleaning fluids.

- Pack a rubber doorstop. You can prop a door open in order to keep an eye on a playing toddler, or hear a sleeping child, or stop it swinging on little fingers. Also take a baby monitor – you can put the parent end out with you on a balcony or terrace, and enjoy an evening meal or drink together without disturbing your baby but in the knowledge that she is safe.

As for bedding, if you can, bring a portable cot with you. At the very least, bring your baby's own bedding.

- If you have to rely on a hotel or self-catering apartment cot, do a careful safety check. Some are old and pre-date safety regulations. It is advisable that you check that:

  ○ Screws and bolts are not missing, loose or bent.

  ○ Your child cannot release safety catches.

  ○ Slats are no more than $2^3/_8$ inches apart, or loose, cracked or missing. If sides are mesh, check it is not torn or has holes.

  ○ Head and footboards are solid, without cutouts, and that there are no sharp or jagged edges.

  ○ The mattress fits snugly on a solid support that is attached to the head and footboards, and that there is a fitted cot sheet. Folded adult sheets are a hazard, as are pillows, and bedding that is too heavy or soft.

- If your baby will be taking naps outside in a pram or buggy, remember that heat and sun can kill. Provide a sun canopy or umbrella, position the buggy in the shade, apply sun cream (rays can burn even in shade) and let your baby drink lots of water before and after sleeping.

That said, try not to become too stressed that your baby will not be safe. These checks need doing right at the start of your holiday – once done, you and your baby can relax and enjoy yourselves. It doesn't take long to create a safe, secure holiday environment.

> **"** We holidayed with our twins when they were about a year old – camping in France. It was certainly an experience! We were actually very surprised how easy it turned out to be, but there was one night where Robert just wouldn't stop crying and was keeping the whole campsite awake – John ended up driving round the French countryside for half the night in his pyjamas with Robert sound asleep in the back. We were very pleased he wasn't pulled over by the police! **"**
>
> Trisha, mother to Hannah and Robert, three

6

Night-time Troubleshooting

" If your baby is "beautiful and perfect, never cries or fusses, sleeps on schedule and burps on demand, an angel all the time," you're the grandma. **"**

Theresa Bloomingdale

Sometimes, despite all your planning and hard work, despite your best positive attitude and calm aura, despite weeks or even months of your child settling seemingly permanently into a good sleep routine... it all goes horribly wrong. Suddenly, out of the blue, you seem to be back where you started. It might start insidiously, a gradual slipping of routines, the odd night of unsettled sleep segueing into a whole run of disrupted nights, a tired and irritable baby, and an equally tired and irritable you. Or it might come upon you with a bang – one minute everything seems to be going along swimmingly, and the next all hell breaks loose and you are hit between the eyes with a sleep drama you have no idea how to deal with.

Sleep troubles can hit any baby, and any family – regardless of which *Baby Sleep Bible* approach you might be following.

So this chapter will take a look at some of the more common night-time disruptions and offer some good general advice that will apply to any kind of sleepers – but look at the end of the chapter for some soothing troubleshooting tips which will help you specifically with your chosen approach.

Sleep problems fall into two main camps. The first are physical. These might include fairly easy to treat ailments such as:

- Ear infections
- Yeast and urinary tract infections
- Respiratory infections
- Parasitic infections

And more complicated physical disorders, such as:

- Sleep apnoea, a breathing disorder that occurs during sleep. Some of the symptoms are snoring, breathing pauses, mouth breathing, restlessness and daytime sleepiness.

- Restless legs syndrome, a neurological disorder characterised by a creepy-crawly feeling in the legs at bedtime which makes children feel a need to move their legs or run around.

- Acid reflux; gastro-oesophageal reflux (GOR) or gastro-oesophageal reflux disease (GORD)

- Colic

- Allergies such as cow's milk allergy

- Teething

- Bruxism (grinding or clenching teeth while sleeping)

The second main area of sleep problems are psychological, and often brought on by external disruption such as a house move, family problems, friendship problems, school problems, or major developmental milestones such as toilet training or starting nursery. Experts, however, also view these sleep disorders as a normal part of physical development, so just because your child displays signs of one of the following doesn't necessarily mean there is an underlying problem or fear. These can include:

- Nightmares, which are common between the ages of three and six. These are a normal part of development. Sometimes nightmares are about monsters or scary creatures, and sometimes they are specifically about an event which might have worried or scared them, such as getting lost or being afraid of a dog.

- Night terrors, which are similar to nightmares but result in a child screaming, but not being alert and not able to recognise you, even though they may seem awake.

- Sleepwalking, where a child may get up and move around but is not awake or aware of what they are doing.

- Separation anxiety. This kicks in around six months of age, when a baby's brain starts to mature so that they become more aware of their own feelings, and they form a strong emotional attachment to their primary caregiver. Babies who previously slept well at night might wake and, instead of settling back to sleep, feel more needy and anxious about your absence.

So, what can you do to help your child and restore night-time peace if any of the above occurs?

PHYSICAL ISSUES

Your first port of call with any of these problems has to be your GP or paediatrician. You will of course develop your own parental instinct about your baby's health – gradually you will find yourself able to judge when an ailment is merely irritating or low-grade, and when it is odd or worrying and needs a professional opinion. But if you are ever in any doubt – any doubt at all – consult your doctor. No doctor will mind seeing a baby or young child, even if a condition turns out to be easily dealt with at home. If you look at or hold your baby and feel uneasy, pick up the phone.

Obviously, if your child has an infection of any kind, such as the ones listed above, she will need treatment from your doctor in any case. Once the underlying infection has been treated, you will probably find that, with a little extra bedtime settling and an ordered return to your usual methods, she will slip easily back into her good sleeping habits.

As for the second category of more complicated physical disorders, let's look at them one-by-one.

Sleep apnoea

Sleep apnoea is a potentially serious disorder in which breathing is interrupted repeatedly during sleep. There are three kinds:

- Obstructive sleep apnoea (OSA), which is caused by a blockage or collapse of the upper airway
- Central sleep apnoea, in which the brain fails to send a signal to the muscles to breathe
- Mixed apnoea, which is a combination of the two

Central sleep apnoea is more common in babies, and OSA is more common in adults and in children over one year, and in children with Down's syndrome and other congenital conditions which affect the upper airway. Sleep apnoea is also much more common in babies born prematurely.

Babies with sleep apnoea stop breathing during sleep. In a sleep lab, a 'pause' for a baby is 20 seconds or more without a breath, and in older children it's 10 seconds. A baby might gasp or gag as they finally take a breath, and may also turn blue.

Remember that it is normal for babies who are less than six months old to experience what doctors call 'periodic breathing' – where your baby breathes fast for a period, then more slowly, then pauses for up to 15 seconds before breathing normally again. This isn't harmful – it's quite common.

However, if the pauses are longer or the colour of your baby is not normal, you will need to see an expert. The specialist may do a variety of tests to measure the amount of oxygen in your baby's blood, and to monitor your baby's breathing and heart rate. They may also take an X-ray. All these tests are painless. If your doctor thinks that your baby has sleep apnoea, they may suggest using a sleep monitor at home to keep track of her breathing and heart rate, or may prescribe medication to stimulate her central nervous system.

Sleep apnoea is more common in premature babies. Some children with severe obstructive apnoea need to use a CPAP (continuous positive airway pressure) machine, which keeps their airway open during sleep by blowing air into the nose via a mask.

Restless legs syndrome

Restless legs syndrome is often described by children as 'creepy crawlies' or 'ouchies'. It can have a significant effect on a child's sleep patterns.

Experts now think that this condition, which may be genetically inherited, could be linked to low levels of iron in the blood. It is worth talking to your doctor about this, because it can be treated with certain drugs in severe cases. You shouldn't add iron supplements to your child's diet without professional advice – the iron connection is not yet proven, and you should never supplement your child's diet with any drug or vitamin unless a doctor has prescribed it.

> 66 The low iron theory is just one of many theories and may apply to some people but certainly not all. Iron overdose in small children can be fatal and care should be taken never to leave vitamin supplements lying around and certainly not to give children the impression that they are sweets.
>
> Sara Warren, midwife 99

Acid reflux (GOR and GORD)

All babies experience some degree of gastro-oesophageal reflux (GOR). But some get it more than others, and it is known that reflux episodes disturb sleep and lead to waking. This happens because the muscle at the lower end of the oesophagus (the food pipe) is too weak to keep the milk in the baby's stomach, so it comes back up along with some stomach acid, which causes a painful burning feeling.

Common symptoms in infants are repeated vomiting, spitting up, coughing, inconsolable crying especially when laid down flat, thrashing and arching the back when feeding, failure to gain adequate weight, refusing food, belching and burping, frequent ear infections or sinus congestion, bad breath and rancid or acid smelling nappies.

GOR is classified as a disease (gastro-oesophageal reflux disease or GORD) when it causes:

- Resistance to feeding
- Blood in the vomit or stool
- Iron deficiency anaemia
- Irritability due to inflamed oesophagus
- Failure to thrive

With both GOR and GORD, you can help your baby and reduce their symptoms by avoiding acidic foods and by keeping them in an upright position for about 20 minutes after feeding. If you think your baby has this problem, see your doctor, who will probably advise medical tests which can help diagnose GORD. If the condition is severe, doctors may prescribe certain medicines that can help. However, most children seem to grow out of this by the time they reach one year.

Colic

Colic has something of an air of mystery about it. People are usually rather unclear as to what colic actually is – but equally emphatic that their baby has it when they cry miserably for several hours every evening, often beginning and ending at the same times every day like clockwork. I could time my clocks by Charlie – he began to scream persistently at precisely 5pm every afternoon, and carried on until about 8.30pm or 9pm before going to sleep. This went on until he was about three months old, at which stage he promptly stopped crying altogether and started a 7pm bedtime.

Colic – discomfort or stress which is seemingly impossible to ease and which causes inconsolable distress to your baby, usually in the evenings – is probably the one thing which causes most daily anguish to new parents. It is exhausting and demoralising and disrupts your and your baby's routine.

If your baby cries for more than three hours a day continuously, for more than three days a week, they probably have colic.

Some experts feel that a baby who has colic is over-stimulated, and has trouble winding down from all the stress they have endured throughout the day. Their stress reliever is to cry, but instead of calming them down, the crying often winds them up further until they are unable to let go. Other experts feel that there is some physical abdominal (tummy) discomfort added to this, which may be linked to GOR.

> **❝** I think Nick used to wind himself up, and make himself more and more upset. It was so hard for me to see him do this to himself. We found that by including a relaxing bath in his evening routine, he was a lot more relaxed when we lay him down and reduced his crying. **❞**
>
> Sarah, mother to Nicholas, six months

What can you do if your baby has colic?

- Remember that colic is not harmful, so don't worry too much. Try to get a break – ask a relative or friend to step in while you escape from the crying for a short while.

- Try removing certain foods from your own diet if you are breastfeeding – common culprits are cabbage, broccoli, cauliflower, sprouts, parsnips, onions, beans, garlic, apricots, melon, spicy foods, caffeine and alcohol.

- If you are bottle feeding, experiment with bottles designed to reduce the amount of air the baby swallows during a feed, including curved ones, ones with a collapsible bag inside or ones with a vent.

- Carry your baby in a front sling or backpack to calm her.

- Swaddle your baby.

- Keep her moving in a baby swing.

- Use white noise from household appliances such as a tumble dryer, dishwasher or vacuum cleaner – or special CDs of white noise – to calm her.

- Take a shower together – the warm water and noise of the water can be comforting.

There are no medicines to treat colic, but you can try relieving your baby's abdominal symptoms with 'colic drops' or 'gripe water', which you can get over the counter from a chemist.

> George had bad colic until he was about 16 weeks. He'd scream from 6pm–2am. I tried the usual gripe water remedies. Then I finally went to the doctor and said 'I can't cope with this', and she gave me Gaviscon powder which stopped it instantly. If I gave it to him, he was fine — if I missed a night, he'd scream again, so it must have been working.
>
> When he was about two he went through a stage of wanting to be in bed with mummy and daddy. We went through a three night pain barrier — I tried everything from being nice to being cajoling to lying in bed with him until he fell asleep, but when we finally got firm with him we broke it and it stopped.
>
> Nikki, childminder and mother of George, six

Cow's milk allergy

Cow's milk allergy is an intolerance to a protein found in cow's milk, and is thought to affect between 2% and 7% of infants. Most sufferers are babies who are being given formula milk, although breastfed babies can acquire this allergy if the mother consumes milk products.

Symptoms can include vomiting, diarrhoea, abdominal cramps and bloating, and sometimes skin rashes, coughs and a runny nose. Cow's milk allergy can also cause babies to wake more often during the night, experience shorter sleep cycles and a shorter overall sleep time. These symptoms usually improve if cow's milk is removed from the diet – one study found that sleep can actually increase by over 20% within a few weeks of stopping. Soya products are available to replace formula milk in these cases. However, check with your doctor before changing your baby's diet.

Teething

Babies' first molars usually come through between 12 and 15 months. The second molars appear towards the end of the second year. These are big teeth! They take their time to come through, too, so they may cause pain and irritability for quite some time. Things you can do to help are:

- Offer something cold to bite on – make sure it's safe and not small enough to swallow or get stuck in the mouth. You can get teething rings which can be chilled in the fridge or freezer.

- Give children's paracetamol or liquid ibuprofen if your baby is over three months – never give aspirin to a child under 16 years old, because it may cause liver damage (Reye's Syndrome).

- Give teething gels.

- Give lots of cuddles and comfort, and allow to feed for longer than usual or more often than usual if your baby wants to.

Bruxism

Some children grind or clench their teeth while sleeping. It's usually not a problem, but can lead to restlessness and to damage to the teeth. Ask your dentist for advice – sometimes they may recommend a plastic mouth guard to prevent damage.

PSYCHOLOGICAL, STRESS-RELATED AND OTHER ISSUES

Nightmares

Just like adults, children dream when they are in REM (rapid eye movement) sleep, which happens four to five times a night. Some of these dreams are not remembered, and some are frightening enough to wake the child. They usually begin when a child is about three years old, and are common between three and eight when their fantasy life is more active. She most commonly occur later in the night, and if your child has one, she will normally be wide awake and responsive afterwards, and often able to recall details of the nightmare the following morning.

The occasional nightmare is absolutely normal. If, however, your child has a sudden increase in the number of nightmares, this can be a response to something they are anxious about. Other triggers can be a change in routine, such as moving house or starting a new preschool or school, or a death in the family. Sometimes they are simply a response to a scary television show or story.

What can you do if your child has a nightmare?

- Reassure her it was just a dream and wasn't real. Give hugs, search her room for monsters if she wants you too, don't 'pooh-pooh' her fears but calmly reassure her there is nothing wrong.

- Leave discussing the details until the morning. Go through your usual sleep-time routine until she falls asleep again.

- In future, avoid television at least an hour before bedtime

- Avoid scary bedtime stories, even for boys

- Suggest she draws a picture of the dream to help her tell you what it was about – this will probably mean she won't have the same nightmare again.

Night terrors

Children from age two to six are most prone to night terrors, and they are thought to affect around 15% of all children. Night terrors are different from nightmares in that the child won't wake up or be aware of you. They will often be highly distressed, screaming, or even hallucinating. They will usually sit bolt upright with eyes wide open in fear and panic, will be sweating, breathing fast and have a rapid heart rate. They are usually impossible to console or comfort.

Night terrors typically last from five to 30 minutes and afterwards children usually return to normal sleep. Unlike nightmares, they usually occur early in the night – about one to four hours after going to sleep.

It is thought that a predisposition to night terrors might be genetically inherited. Other triggers might include emotional stress during the previous day, constipation, or a high fever. Children usually grow out of night terrors.

What should you do?

- Don't try to wake your child – you will just cause more panic. Just make sure they are safe, comfort them if you can, and lay them back down to sleep.

- Stick to a good bedtime routine – night terrors often happen to children who are overtired.

- For children who get frequent night terrors, it might help if you wake them up before the time they usually get one. This is thought to interrupt or alter the sleep cycle and stop a terror from happening.

66 All of my children have suffered night terrors and I found the best way to deal with them was to pick the child up and take them downstairs to a well-lit kitchen or living room, give them a cuddle, talk normally to them about ordinary things such as what I was doing and perhaps offer them something to drink. The 'normality' of everything seemed to calm them down and bring them out of it sooner and they'd have no trouble getting

back to sleep again when gently put back to bed afterwards.

Sara Warren, midwife

"

Sleepwalking

Sleepwalking is similar to night terrors – they are a partial awakening and they also occur a few hours after children go to sleep. Even if they are walking down the stairs or around the house, they are not awake or aware of what they are doing. Do not wake your child up if you find her sleepwalking. Just guide her back to bed and make sure she is safe. You can also:

- Wake her before she usually begins to sleepwalk, as with night terrors.

- Use stair gates and remove sharp furniture to minimise the risk of her injuring herself while sleepwalking.

" We had a funny time when Ashley kept getting out of bed and sleepwalking. Someone told us not to wake her up, so we'd just steer her back to bed and sit with her until she seemed to sleep properly again – her breathing settled down. Apparently waking them up can really frighten them.

Tom, father of Rebecca, eight, Ashley, five, and Vincent, three

"

Separation anxiety

This will naturally abate as your baby grows and develops. Until then, you should be prepared for a little extra comforting if your baby awakes during the night, and perhaps the introduction of a transitional object such as a comforter or blankie.

Other tips to ease the pain of you leaving while they sleep are:

- Lavender drops on a hanky in their bed or cot to soothe them.

- A recording of your voice reading stories or singing lullabies, playing while they go to sleep.

- Accessories which give off light, such as fairy lights or luminous moons and stars. One person I know even put a back-lit fish tank in their child's room, which mesmerised them to sleep every night!

- Using your baby monitor back-to-front, with the baby end downstairs and the parents' end in your child's room, so that she can hear you moving about and chatting and listen to the reassuring noises of your presence in the house.

Remember that separation anxiety is a normal stage of development, and while it can be challenging to be so 'in demand' for a while, is nothing to worry about. Of course, your priority when dealing with any kind of night-time problem or sleep disorder will be to establish exactly what is disturbing your child, whether the cause of it is physically or mentally harmful, and if necessary how this can be treated or at least alleviated. But once you are on the path to sorting this out, you will naturally want your baby to return to the reassuring, comforting normality of their usual sleep routine. So what can *Baby Sleep Bible* parents do to get back on track?

> **❝** There are times when your sleep is disrupted due to various reasons and I think that one has to accept that it's part of parenthood. Get over it! If the girls wake, I talk to them about something they enjoy. In India's case, she likes bouncy castles and at times she has woken in the morning and stated that she dreamed of a bouncy castle and she jumped and jumped. So if she does wake in the night, I tell her to picture that bouncy castle and start bouncing on it!
>
> Dalvinder, mother of Amber, five, India, three, and Jasmine, 11 months **❞**

BACK TO NATURE

The good news is that if your baby is experiencing temporary sleep difficulties, she already has you on hand for extra comfort if she is co-sleeping with you. The sheer presence of a parent can calm a baby, regulate their heart rhythms, and reduce stress.

The downsides of this are:

- If your baby is waking in the night in your bed, you will be exhausted too.

- If your baby is ill or teething and has a high temperature, she may overheat if she is pressed up next to you.

So, what you can do is modify your Back to Nature approach slightly until you come through this phase. This doesn't mean moving your baby into a cot if you are not ready to do so. But it could mean buying a 'baby nest', which sits on the mattress next to you and gives a baby with a temperature slightly more space and airflow. Or it could mean moving the baby from the main bed to a 'sidecar' cot or Moses basket for a few nights, or an older child from the main bed to a mattress next to you.

Either way, your baby will be able to continue to follow her usual routine. And if she needs to take extra naps in the day to compensate for a disturbed night, she is well placed to follow her Back to Nature approach for naps downstairs or around the house as usual – with a little extra cuddling thrown in.

> ❝ Teething always makes their sleep erratic and I think you just learn to ride with it. Some pain relieving medication before bed is good and some gel for their gums if they wake. Fionn had the worst colic, though I wonder now how much night time crying was actually due to over-handling and not leaving him alone a bit!
>
> Fionn woke with night terrors at about two years and I think it's more of a boy thing. Sometimes he would get quite hysterical and I would have to put the light on to snap him out of it. Again – riding through it with love and patience is all you can do!
>
> Lisa, mother of Fionn, three, and
> Bridget, 10 months ❞

BY THE CLOCK

The good news for By the Clock families is that a child who has sleep problems has a solid and reassuring routine to fall back on. The trick is not to become unnerved if timings slip slightly – bending your routine to cope with temporary glitches will not ruin everything. On the contrary, your secure and independent baby will probably cope better than many with illness or upsets, because everything else in her life is reliable and running smoothly.

Having a baby in a separate sleeping space or their own bedroom is also helpful if she is waking often at night-time, because parents have somewhere she can retreat to for a good period of sleep, even if they take it in turns. This will help with coping the next day with an unusually tired or sick baby. What you might have to consider, though, is that a child having night-time traumas will need a little extra comfort and support. So you might:

- Take extra time for cuddles and comforting stories at bedtime.

- Spend longer on their pre-bedtime routine such as baths and feeds, in order to give comfort and create a reassuring atmosphere in their sleeping space.

- Not worry if they try to creep into bed with you. It is natural for an infant to seek extra comfort if in pain or anxious. A cuddle in your bed doesn't mean you are suddenly co-sleeping. Just have a nice loving cuddle, then help your child back to her cot or bed and use your normal sleep routine to get her to settle herself.

- Consider using controlled crying techniques once your baby is well again, just to re-establish your usual sleep times and patterns.

> ❝ Phoebe has pretty bad colic. We find her baby swing helps in the early evening. But we're hoping she's going to grow out of it soon. I think that going onto solids, starting a proper routine and sticking to it will help – it did with Sara.
>
> Gemma, mother of Sara, two, and
> Phoebe, two months ❞

FLEXI-SLEEPING

Flexi-Sleepers will find that they are well-placed for coping with unusual disruptions to routines and situations – after all, they have spent the whole of their tiny lives preparing for the unexpected. So all you have to do when faced with a temporary sleep disruption is to reinforce that 'chain of constants' that goes hand-in-hand with all daily activities anyway. If you like, you and your child might choose to add something into your 'chain' if it helps her to overcome a certain anxiety-related disturbance such as nightmares:

- A 'monster-scaring teddy', who comes out after a nightmare to check the room and make sure it is safe to go back to sleep.

- A special night light or lamp, which can be turned on after a bad dream to chase away the shadows.

You will probably find that your child copes better than most with sleep problems – but just be aware that she might need slightly more 'normality' than usual for a little while if things are very disrupted. Are there any ways in which you can minimise the ups and downs for a week or two until she has found her feet again? Or are there any recent events or changes that have been unusually difficult for her to deal with – after all, even though your child is now a master at coping with the unpredictable, she is still only a child, and even a change which seems relatively small and insignificant to you might be tipping the balance for her.

Sit down when you have a peaceful moment and ask your child how things are going when you are not with her. Maybe draw pictures together of what you do when you are apart – you might draw your office or your car, she might draw her nursery or childminder's house. Children can often express worries more easily through drawing, dolls and role play than with words. And it might just be that a simple tweak to your week will set her back on track.

> **"** When you're on your own with a child who isn't sleeping and it's the middle of the night, you can feel like you're going out of your mind. My lifesaver was going on message boards like the ones on Mumsnet. I made real friends who got me through – it's amazing who else is online at 3am!
>
> Kim, mother of Sasha, two **"**

MULTIPLE MADNESS

It may not come as any consolation to you that when one of your babies is poorly or teething, it's very likely the other one will be too – so if they co-sleep in a bed or share a room, there isn't much point in separating them. However, if one of your babies is experiencing a longer-term problem which is disrupting the sleep of a sibling who would otherwise be sleeping perfectly well, it might well be an idea to give her extra space, whether that is a separate Moses basket or cot in the same room, or a room of her own.

The problems you have, which are in addition to those experienced parents of single babies are:

- You will probably be exhausted and running on empty anyway, let alone once one or both or all of your babies start experiencing disrupted night-times. Therefore you must take measures to protect your own sleep too, even if that means sleeping further away from your babies than usual for a while.

- Your 'disrupted' baby may react even more poorly if suddenly separated from the reassuring presence of a sibling – so go carefully if suddenly deciding on separate rooms. It might be better to opt for separate cribs next to each other for a while, and if you still wish to move them to separate rooms, gradually move one crib to the other side of the room, and then near to the door, etc before making the final step.

- Not only do you have to consider your 'disrupted' baby, but you have to monitor the effect of the disruption on the other baby or babies too. Even your peaceful baby might become disturbed or anxious if their sibling is ill or has a disorder or has been moved away from them – don't forget to reassure her too and offer comfort objects such as a blankie.

Remember too to ask for help.

It is easy to become marooned in a kind of lonely treacle when you are exhausted and surrounded by tired and irritable children. Get out of your house, talk to your friends, and ask willing helpers to muck in with simple, practical tasks such as picking up nappies or supplies, or cooking a stew for tea, or taking a baby out for a 30-minute walk in the buggy. Often people aren't sure what they can actually do to help – specific tasks are usually greeted with enthusiasm.

> Someone once told me to sell off all the family jewels and hire a night nanny! We never did. But what I would say is that the most difficult time of all with twins is when one of them is poorly. It's almost worse than both being poorly at the same time, because you're constantly trying to keep the okay one settled and asleep rather than just accepting the chaos. It really does help if you can get someone to help for a night or two – a helpful granny maybe? Also, try to keep your sense of humour – Matt and I used to work our way through a DVD comedy box set to keep ourselves from spiralling into despair!

Jenny, mother of Luke and Perry, seven

A Few Final Words

❝ When I was a community midwife I could usually tell which mothers were more likely to become completely exhausted even to the point of postnatal depression, these were the ones who were attempting to be superwoman. They were overly concerned by how clean and tidy their homes were and determined to keep up the same pace of life they had before the arrival of a new baby. Sleep is more important than tidiness and if anyone tries to make you think otherwise – they're an idiot and not to be listened to! Find whichever way works for you all to get the most sleep that you can, including developing the knack of napping with impunity. This too will pass and before you know it your tiny tyrant will be stealing your mascara and borrowing the keys to your car.

Sara Warren, midwife **❞**

I hope that this book will give you the hope – that no parent needs to be a superhero; that good enough is good enough; that all troubles pass eventually; and that a good night's sleep is something you can achieve for both you and your baby. Also; that whichever way you set about achieving this, you have the right to do so without fear of being judged, or 'doing it wrong', or inadvertently bestowing on your child a lifetime of neuroses; that every baby is different and sleeps differently, but that every baby can and should and wants to sleep; and that you are the best judge of what your baby needs and likes, so trust yourself.

Know too that when a parent looks upon a sleeping child, there is and never will be any feeling quite like it – look forward to it, soak it up, savour it. You have helped them rest.

A sleeping baby is a small soul on display. And you are that soul's guardian. Be proud of yourself. And then go take a nap quickly, before they wake up!

the parenting & family health experts

Get 30% off your next purchase...

We are publishers of a growing **parenting and family health** range of books. We pride ourselves on our friendly and accessible approach whilst providing you with sensible, non-preachy information. This is what makes us **different from other publishers**.

And we are keen to **find out what you think** about our book.

If you love this book **tell us why** and tell your friends. And if you think we could do better, **let us know**. Your thoughts and opinions are important to us and help us produce the best books we possibly can.

As a **thank you** we'll give you 30% off your next purchase. Write to us at **info@whiteladderpress.co.uk** and we'll send you an online voucher by return.

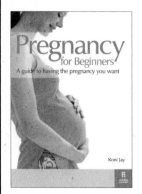  

Come and visit us at **www.whiteladderpress.co.uk**